the Forth Naturalist and Historian

Volume 17

Forth Naturalist and Historian, volume 17

Published by the Forth Naturalist and Historian, a University/Central Regional Council collaboration, and an approved charity. The University, Stirling, 1994.

ISSN 0309-7560

ISBN 1 898008 02 7

Supported by BP in Scotland

Cover photograph Robert Louis Stevenson at Vailima dictating to step daughter Belle (Writers Museum)

Printed by Meigle Printers Ltd., Tweedbank Industrial Estate, Galashiels. Set in Zapf Calligraphic on 90gsm Fyneprint Paper with Cream Astralux 290 cover.

MINERAL RESCUE COLLECTING AT THE ALVA SILVER MINES

Brian Jackson
National Museums of Scotland

Again, after almost 225 years, the old familiar sounds of industry returned to the Silver Glen at Alva in April of this year. The long abandoned silver and cobalt mines have received much attention in recent years. Mineral collectors, researchers, geologists and students have visited the old spoil heaps and slowly their contents are being removed. Surprisingly, there are hardly any mineral specimens from the old workings in museums. In order to safeguard material for future research or display, the National Museums of Scotland (NMS) in conjunction with researchers and local mineralogical activists undertook, with the permission of the landowner, a rescue collecting dig.

Guided by Dr Stephen Moreton, who has studied the old mines and their history, the old dumps were excavated using a JCB and sometimes by hand. Water was pumped from the burn to a sluice box made by the NMS joiners from old 1910 diagrams. The excavated gravel was washed in this and the heavy minerals recovered.

Surprisingly, even at depth, there was very little mineralisation left in the spoil heaps. Barite, the main constituent of the mineral veins was the most abundant. However it was the metallic ores and their alteration products that were of most interest and there was hardly any evidence of these. Pink coloured erythrite, an alteration product of the primary cobalt ore, was the easiest to recognise.

Only a few ore specimens larger than 2-3 cm were recovered. Most material was smaller than this but still contained good silver crystals and cobalt ore. The type of cobalt ore in the veins has always been subject to conjecture. A cobaltite (cobalt arsenide with sulphur) specimen in the Glasgow Museum and Art Gallery, Kelvingrove, is labelled as coming from Alva. The locality has always been questioned by those familiar with worldwide cobaltite occurrences. All cobalt ore specimens collected during the dig were clinosafflorite: sulphur deficient cobalt arsenide. It seems likely therefore that the main cobalt ore at Alva was clinosafflorite.

Besides the metal ores, representative specimens of barite were recovered and alteration products of the cobalt arsenic metal ore: erythrite and tyrolite. Some rock specimens showing the brecciated vein structure were also removed. All these specimens are available at the NMS to researchers and the public.

The spoil heaps have been reinstated and perhaps this successful rescue collecting operation may lead to future work on the veins themselves.

Heavy mineral separation – sluice box in action, Moreton and Jackson.

Sorting and selecting material excavated.

NMS working party with Stephen Moreton on the left, and the 'sluice'.

THE WEATHER OF 1993

S J Harrison
University of Stirling

The Weather Year

January set the scene for what was to be an eventful year. Severe storms early in the month drove the tanker 'Braer' on to the rocks of the Shetlands on January 5th, and by the 11th blizzards had closed the A9 north of Dunblane for two days. When the snow melted in heavy rain some of the worst floods this century caused extensive damage in central Scotland, and parts of Perth and Stirling were under water. By contrast, February was abnormally dry but there was an extensive late snowfall over Scotland in May. Over the latter half of the year, temperatures were well below normal, reversing recent trends. Winter snow, as early as October in parts of Scotland, brought a welcome cover on the ski slopes and for the first time for more than two decades it wasn't necessary to be on the summit of Ben Nevis to experience a white Christmas. In the following summary of the weather during each month, the figures for temperature and rainfall refer to Parkhead weather station unless indicated otherwise.

January. Wet and very windy.

The wind was strong south-westerly until the 10th, occasionally reaching storm force, and several days were blustery and wet. Snow persisted in a fresh to strong south-westerly wind between the 11th and 14th closing many main roads but most of the snow had disappeared from the Forth valley by the end of the 13th. Milder air came in from the south-west late on the 14th and by 09.00 hrs on the 15th 40.3 mm of rain had fallen in Bridge of Allan (33.1 mm Parkhead). Local rivers, which were already running high by the early morning of the 15th, became more swollen during the day as rain continued to fall. The Teith, Forth and Allan all overtopped their banks and flooding persisted until the 19th. Conditions were worsened by gales which caused local damage on the 15th, 16th and 17th. There were severe gales in Scotland on the evening of the 21st which caused some structural damage. The Allan was in flood again on the 24th. The weather entered a welcome calmer phase from the 25th and the next five days were dull with occasional light rain.

February. Mild and very dry.

Night temperatures fell to below -4.0 °C at the beginning of the month but mild south-westerly air improved temperatures, which reached 13.0 °C on the 7th. Night minimum temperatures were unseasonal and fell to only 8.6 °C on the 13th. After the 11th Scotland was affected by damp southerly air which brought occasional drizzle but it became fresher and brighter on the 16th. By the 26th the wind had changed to northerly and brief flurries of snow indicated a return to winter after what had been a long spell of mild and dry weather. Snow was lying above 152m by the end of the month. The most remarkable feature of February was the lack of rain, which barely exceeded 7 mm in the Stirling area.

March. Cold start but mild and wet mid-month.

Cold weather continued for the first four days but there was a rise of more than 4 °C in the daytime temperature by the 5th. The weather, however, remained changeable but relatively dry until the 10th. The maximum temperature reached 15.4 °C at Bridge of Allan on the 12th. The temperature fell quickly on the 18th and sleet and snow returned after a week of mild weather. The wind was fresh to strong westerly on the 19th and 20th becoming north-westerly on the 21st. By the evening of the 22nd, rain and sleet had turned to snow, which was lying as a light cover by the morning of the 23rd. Under clearing skies the night temperature fell, reaching -5.0 °C in Bridge of Allan by the morning of the 26th. The weather became milder and wetter and 30.2 mm of rain was registered over the 28th and 29th, 21.3 mm falling on the latter in a fresh southerly wind, which was gusting gale force by the 30th.

April. Dull and wet but relatively mild.

Usually one of the driest months, April was dominated by a sequence of rain-bearing weather systems from the west which maintained very unsettled weather with occasional bright and sunny interludes. The rain was often very heavy and between the 8th and 9th 26.7 mm of rain was recorded (33.1 mm Bridge of Allan). However the cloud cover served to keep night temperatures well above freezing. The weather in Scotland after the 10th was generally dull, while in England and Wales thunderstorms were widespread on the 12th and 13th. The 25th and 26th were exceptionally dull with low cloud down to 500 ft. The clouds cleared by the 28th and the daytime temperature rose to reach a remarkable 20.0 °C on the 30th. However, in the absence of a cloud cover the night temperatures fell and a slight frost was registered in Bridge of Allan early on the 29th (-0.2 °C).

May. Cloudy and wet after a bright start. Cold mid-month.

The weather was mostly sunny at the beginning of the month, temperatures reaching 20.0 °C on the 2nd and 3rd. Clearing skies resulted in night frosts down in the Forth valley, the temperature falling to -1.4 °C in Bridge of Allan between the 3rd and 4th. Torrential rain fell after midnight on the 7th. The 13th saw a return to wintery conditions as cold arctic air swept southwards across Scotland bringing snow to the hills. The daytime temperature reached only 5.8 °C on the 13th and over Scotland as a whole the 14th was one of the coldest May days on record this century. After the 13th the following five days were very unsettled with a total rainfall of 60.3 mm. A light easterly airstream developed after the 18th and daytime temperatures rose to 25.8 °C on the 23rd after a dull start to the day. The east coast was, however, cool and misty at times. The weather was briefly sunny and warm on the 28th before a wet Whitsun weekend, 27.5 mm of rain falling during the 48 hrs 29-30th.

June. Cloudy and damp.

Unsettled weather continued for the first two days but daytime temperatures rose slowly in a light south-westerly breeze and topped 20.0 °C from the 6th onwards. Thundery rain fell from 18.00 hrs on the 9th after an unpleasantly muggy day (25.9 °C). From the 14th the weather was wet and generally unsettled. After a wet evening on the 25th daytime temperatures rose under a relatively clear sky, reaching 24.3 °C on the 29th (27.3 °C in Bridge of Allan).

July. Cool and damp after a dry start.

There were small amounts of rain on the 7th and 8th and on the 9th and 10th there were some remarkable falls in temperature. The maximum temperature reached only 14.0 °C in Stirling on the 10th, which is 6 °C below the monthly average. Under clear night skies the air temperature fell to 3.3 °C by the morning of the 13th. Unsettled weather persisted between the 15th and 19th and heavy thundery rain fell on both the 16th (10.8 mm) and 19th (12.5 mm). Fog along the east coast on the 16th caused several traffic accidents. Unsettled weather persisted until the end of the month, although rainfall amounts were very small.

August. Cool and mostly dry.

The first few days were cloudy and wet but as the skies cleared the minimum temperature had fallen to 6.2 °C (4.4 °C in Bridge of Allan) by the morning of the 6th. Unsettled westerly weather prevailed until the 14th, bringing more substantial rainfall and the 14th was the month's wettest day (14.5 mm). From the 15th, the weather was generally dry for the rest of the month. Daytime temperatures rose to almost respectable summer levels by the 27th (20.5 °C), often after early morning mist had cleared. The 31st was particularly warm, reaching a maximum of 23.4 °C by early afternoon (26.4 °C Bridge of Allan), but late evening saw the first signs of autumn as ground fog began to form over low-lying damper ground.

September. Cool and mostly dry at first.

The weather was calm and dry for the first five days although a little light rain fell on the 3rd. A fresh easterly wind developed from the 6th but no rain fell until the 8th after which the next two days were damp with occasional sunny periods. After the 15th there was a spell of dry weather but rain returned late on the 18th. The 19th was the month's wettest day with 18.6 mm. Although winds were light to calm from the 22nd there were occasional spells of rain and poor visibility. However, the skies eventually cleared and the 25th to 28th were sunny days although night temperatures fell below freezing in Bridge of Allan, the first of the autumn frosts.

October. Mild and wet at first, becoming colder.

The weather was unsettled for several days and between the 5th and 10th there was 37.4 mm of rain. Moderate frosts were recorded from the 14th to 19th, falling to -6.5 °C on the 17th (-7.7 °C in Bridge of Allan). Carnwath in Lanarkshire registered -9.9 °C on the same day, the lowest on record for October. Snow showers were an additional hazard in the far north and along the east coast. A cover of 4 cm accumulated at Dyce on the 16th, the first October snow for 20 years. From the 20th the weather was frequently very dull, dense fog forming on the 25th and light drizzle falling on the 31st.

November. Very cold but drier than usual.

After the month's wettest day on the 3rd (12.0 mm), the 4th and 5th were foggy. The 7th and 8th were both very wet days (48 hr total 14.7 mm). The air became much colder on the 9th and by the morning of the 10th the temperature had fallen to -2.5 °C (-3.8 °C in Bridge of Allan) in dense fog. Freezing fog returned again overnight but had cleared by 10.00 hrs on the 11th as less settled weather moved in from the Atlantic. After the 15th, the weather was cold but dry until the 20th. Daytime temperatures remained below 6 °C and there were moderate night frosts. By the 22nd there was a light cover of snow down in the Forth valley. The 23rd and 24th were calm but exceptionally cold, daytime temperatures struggling to rise above 0 °C, and freezing fog was widespread. The *maximum* temperature at Braemar was -8.0 °C on the 24th !! On the 28th a strong south-easterly wind began to blow which was accompanied by driving rain on the 29th (7.6 mm).

December. Mild at first turning colder with snow.

Unsettled weather continued into December and on the 3rd persistent heavy rain fell all day in a strong south-westerly (11.5 mm). By the 7th there were isolated snow showers in cold arctic air with some heavy falls in the Scottish Highlands. Early morning rain on the 8th turned to sleet and snow for a while. The 48 hr rainfall on the 8th and 9th was 31.5 mm. The air tended to be cold until the 17th which meant that rain occasionally turned to snow and the weather had a raw feel to it. However, warm air crossed Scotland from the south-west late on the 17th which resulted in a welcome increase in temperature, reaching 14.0 °C on the 17th, but cold arctic air returned on the 18th. The daytime temperature on the 20th reached only 1.5 °C in Bridge of Allan in a fresh north-easterly. Under clear night skies the temperature fell to the lowest of the year falling below -7.0 °C on the 21st, 22nd and 23rd. There were heavy hoar frosts in the mornings. From the 23rd isolated snow showers occurred as far south as Cornwall and many places experienced their first white Christmas for more than 20 years. Moderate snow fell again on the 28th, which lay to a depth of 2 cm on low ground. However, this melted very quickly in the milder air. Colder weather returned on the 30th and the daytime temperature on the 31st reached only 1.7 °C. The most noteworthy feature of December's weather was that the barometric pressure was very low, the month's average being only 994 mb, 24 mb lower than during November.

Shetland storms and the 'Braer'

The oil tanker 'Braer' lost headway and drifted onto the rocks of the Shetland Islands in a storm force 11 southerly wind on the 5th January 1993. The tanks ruptured and 85000 tonnes of oil poured into the sea, which raised fears of a major ecological disaster. The strong wind whipped up spray from the sea surface and an oily aerosol was driven inland. The tanker lay on the rocks and was pounded by consistently heavy seas for several days which dispersed the oil in the water column thereby limiting the damage to wildlife. By the 10th of January a very intense depression lay between Iceland and the Hebrides, its central pressure fell to below 920 mb for some 15 hours. The depression was the deepest cyclone on record in the North Atlantic, having given rise to what is almost certainly the lowest barometric pressure yet recorded on the planet, apart from tropical storms and tornadoes (Burt 1993). Hurricane force winds (force 12) were forecast for the northern shipping areas. By 18.00 hrs on the 11th winds gusting in excess of 70 knots were reported in the Shetlands, increasing to 80 to 100 knots by 06.00 hrs on the 12th. The Braer gave up the last of its oil and broke up in the mountainous seas.

Burt, S. 1993 Another new North Atlantic low pressure record *Weather* 48 (4) 98-103

January blizzards

A very cold arctic airstream followed in the wake of the intense low pressure of January 10th. Snow began to fall in the very cold westerly winds during the evening of the 10th and by the morning of the 11th there was a thin snow cover across the Forth valley. Snow continued to fall in the strong westerly wind and there were blizzard conditions for much of the 11th, which continued into the 12th. Although accumulations of snow in the Forth valley came to little more than a few centimetres, with some deeper drifts in places, conditions were a great deal worse on slightly higher ground and the A9 north of Dunblane was closed beyond the Keir roundabout for two days. Heavy goods vehicles were held up in Stirling and Blackford until the road could be cleared. Although the temperature increased slightly on the 9th, which melted much of the snow on lower ground, blizzards continued on the higher stretches of several roads and by midday on the 14th, Aviemore, for example, had more than 50 cm of snow. A more general thaw arrived late on the 14th as a warm front crossed Scotland from the south-west, which caused yet more problems.

The Big Flood

The floods which affected Central Region on the 15th, 16th and 17th of January were the worst on record since 1909, and were due to an unfortunate combination of weather events. An increase in temperature, which caused a rapid thaw, together with very heavy overnight rain on the 14th/15th, released a huge volume of water into local streams. Problems were compounded by gales on the 15th and 16th which brought down a large number of trees which not only blocked roads but also clogged streams and rivers with debris. The 48 hour rainfall on the 14th/15th was 49.8 mm. Local rivers were already swollen by the morning of the 15th and levels continued to rise during the day, and also the next day. In the Stirling area, Broomridge, Riverside and the Cornton Road were particularly badly affected and folk were evacuated from parts of Riverside on the morning of Sunday 17th. Callander and Aberfoyle were also flooded and damage to a railway bridge at Forteviot closed the main railway line to Perth. Massive trash was carried along in the flood and when the waters subsided huge tree trunks and large amounts of debris lay stranded some distance away from the river banks. Serious floods also affected the River Tay, and large areas of Perth were under water as river levels rose to more than 6m above normal.

Climate Change

The Global Warming debate now appears to have shifted very much more towards broader issues. The uncertainty in predictive models and in the understanding of climate processes have been stated more explicitly and the words 'may' and 'possible' now appear more frequently in assessments of potential impacts. In the 'The Global Warming Trial' (Radio 4, 17 September) the charge against the scientific community for "acting irresponsibly, causing discredit to the integrity of science..." appears not to have been proven. The report from the Hadley Centre on their 'Transient Climate Change Experiment', which was published in August 1992, predicted a range of climate changes which may be expected in Scotland by the middle of the 21st century.

Summary of predicted climate changes for Western Europe (after Hadley Centre 1992)

0.2°C increase in near-surface temperature per decade near the Atlantic coast.
Decrease in the intensity of very cold spells in winter.
Increased number of hot summers.
Marked decrease (c25%) in the frequency of frosts.
"Over a period of one or two decades natural variability could mask any warming due to increased greenhouse gases".
Increase in annual precipitation of the order of 20%.
Marked reduction in snowfall.
Convective shower precipitation more frequent.
Decrease in the number of rain days ($\geq$ 0.2mm).
Increase in the amount of rain falling on a rain day.
Little change in soil moisture values.
Soils could be slightly drier in summer.
Sulphate aerosols will have a net cooling effect.

There have been several recent conferences on the potential effects of these changes in Scotland. The Highland Green Party organised a conference "The Effects of Global Warming on the Highlands of Scotland" which was held in

Kingussie in April 1993, and the Scottish Climate Change Research Group gathered together reports from ongoing research at a conference "Climate Change – from Impact to Interaction" held in Dundee in January 1994.

An assessment of the effect of changing airflow patterns on the distribution of snow in Scotland was published in 1993 (Harrison 1993). A comparison between a mild 'westerly' winter and a cold 'easterly' winter has shown that snow cover could be reduced by over 60% in eastern Scotland but by less than 50% in western Scotland if the former type of winter were to become more prevalent in a globally warmed climate. However, the situation with regard to snow cover on higher slopes, above 500 m, remains uncertain due to the shortage of snow lie data for these areas.

Hadley Centre 1992 The Hadley Centre Transient Climate Change Experiment Met Office Bracknell.
Harrison, S. J. 1993 Differences in the duration of snow cover on the Scottish ski slopes between mild and cold winters *Scottish Geographical Magazine* 109 (1) 37-44.

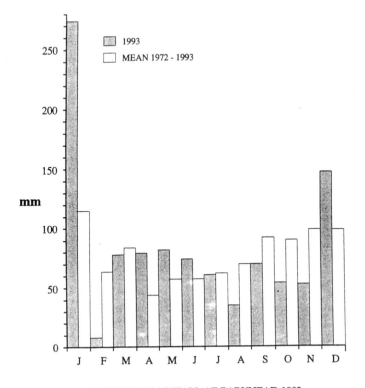

MONTHLY RAINFALL AT PARKHEAD 1993

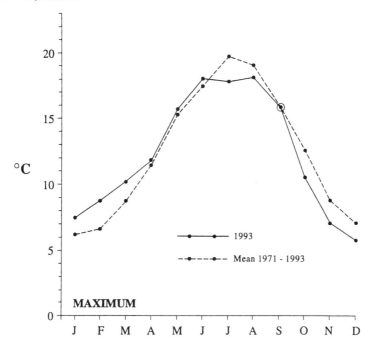

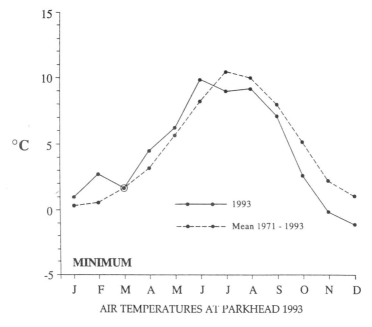

AIR TEMPERATURES AT PARKHEAD 1993

ALPINE FOXTAIL (*Alopecurus borealis* Trin.) IN THE OCHILS

R. W. M. Corner

In June 1989 I found the rare arctic-subarctic grass, Alpine Foxtail (*Alopecurus borealis* Trin., *A. alpinus* Sm.) in two flushes at 600-650m on Ben Buck in the Ochils. This is the lowest range of hills in which this species has been found in the British Isles. Until 1956 it was thought to be confined to high altitudes on the highest Scottish mountains. However in that year Derek Ratcliffe discovered the grass high in the Moffat Hills in Dumfriesshire (Ratcliffe 1959). In 1959 its southern range was further extended by its discovery in the Northern Pennines (Ratcliffe and Eddy 1960). Since then, in 1981, a further record was made from The Cheviot (Corner 1982).

After this latest find it seemed to me that there were several pointers to the Foxtail's possible presence in the Ochils. Firstly, the eastern location, secondly, the relatively high and extensive area of hill country, and thirdly the presence of two arctic alpines common to all the known sites south of the Highlands. The two relevant species are the Alpine Willowherb (*Epilobium anagallidifolium*) and the rare moss *Splachnum vasculosum*. Therefore it was especially rewarding, after a few days search, to find that the grass was indeed present very locally in considerable quantity. It is principally distinguished from the other *Alopecurus* species by the shape of the panicles which are short and broadly cylindrical. They measure 1-3cm long by 7-12cm wide, are greyish green or tinged with purple, and silkily hairy.

Among other local montane plants seen on the Ochils, and common to all the Foxtail's southern localities were the Stiff Edge (*Carex bigelowii*), Chickweed Willowherb (*Epilobium alsinefolium*), Mossy Saxifrage (*Saxifraga hypnoides*), Starry Saxifrage (*S. stellaris*), Bog Stonecrop (*Sedum villosum*), and the moss *Bryum weigelii*.

The history of the Foxtail's discovery and distribution is of considerable interest. It was first discovered exactly 200 years ago by Robert Brown on Lochnagar in 1794, new to science, and is still present there. It was not until exploratory expeditions penetrated into the Arctic regions some years later that the grass was found to be a widespread and relatively common circumpolar and High Arctic species.

This grass is a unique member of our arctic-subarctic flora in that it has never been found in Scandinavia or Iceland. Its nearest localities are in Greenland, Spitzbergen and Arctic Russia. The threat to the Foxtail's survival in the southern localities is from intensive sheep grazing. In the Highlands the increased numbers of deer pose a similar threat. I would hope that the grazing pressures could be reduced and allow this especially interesting grass to survive.

REFERENCES

CORNER, R. W. M. 1982. *Alopecurus alpinus* Sm. in Cheviot. *Watsonia* 14 (2) 228.
HUBBARD, C. E. 1988. Grasses. Penguin Books. 336-7.
RATCLIFFE, D. A. 1959. Montane Plants of the Moffat Hills. *Transactions of the Botanical Society of Edinburgh* 37 (4) 257-71.
RATCLIFFE, D. A. & EDDY, E. 1960. *Alopecurus alpinus* Sm. in Britain. *Proceedings of the Botanical Survey of the British Isles* 3, 389-391.

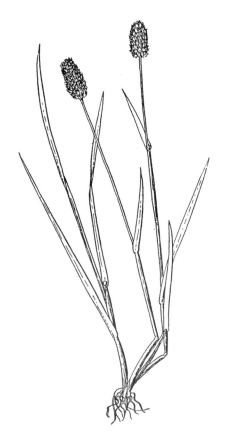

Alpine Foxtail
Alopecurus alpinus. Very rare; Scottish mountains (Hubbard).

WOODLANDS FOR THE COMMUNITY

Alastair Seaman
Eamonn Wall & Co.

Multi Purpose Woodlands

To many people the very word 'forestry' conjures up images of endless ranks of rigid spruce marching across the countryside. Owned by impersonal pension companies or absentee landlords, these 'tree farms' are considered as blots on the landscape and harmful to wildlife with minimal recreational value. Yet although mistakes have undoubtedly been made in the past, this image is more a result of media misrepresentation than present day reality on the ground. In fact, government incentives are now geared to encourage a more responsible multi-objective forestry which recognises that, in addition to providing a sustainable supply of one of our most basic raw materials (wood), forests supply society with a variety of other benefits. They are home to a wide range of plants and animals, provide shelter for homes, livestock and crops and, if sensitively designed, can contribute significantly to landscapes. Forests can absorb heavy recreation pressure and accommodate a wide range of leisure pursuits from nature trails to mountain biking, pony trekking to field archery. They also lock up large volumes of carbon dioxide, one of the most important 'Greenhouse' gases.

Growing recognition of these wider values has led to grant incentives which encourage the creation of multi-purpose woodlands close to centres of population. Known as Community Woodlands, these areas are not only designed primarily for the local community but often involve their substantial input into design, planting and management. Last year a total of 65 hectares (160 acres) of new community woodlands were planted throughout Scotland, 74% of which were in the Perth Conservancy (incorporating Fife, Tayside and Central Regions). This article briefly describes the process of creating these woods and looks at some considerations in their design and management.

The Process

The Forestry Authority allocates its budget for community woodlands at the level of District Councils (Forestry Authority 1993). Each Council has produced a 'community woodland plan' which is essentially a map highlighting areas of greatest potential for these new woods (Figure 1). Suitable proposals to plant in these areas are usually accepted although other areas close to centres of population may also be eligible. When a landowner in an eligible area expresses an interest in the scheme, the first step is usually to canvas local opinion, often by contacting Community Councils, Residents Associations and local amenity/conservation organisations. If there is general enthusiasm for the idea, the next step would be to put together an initial

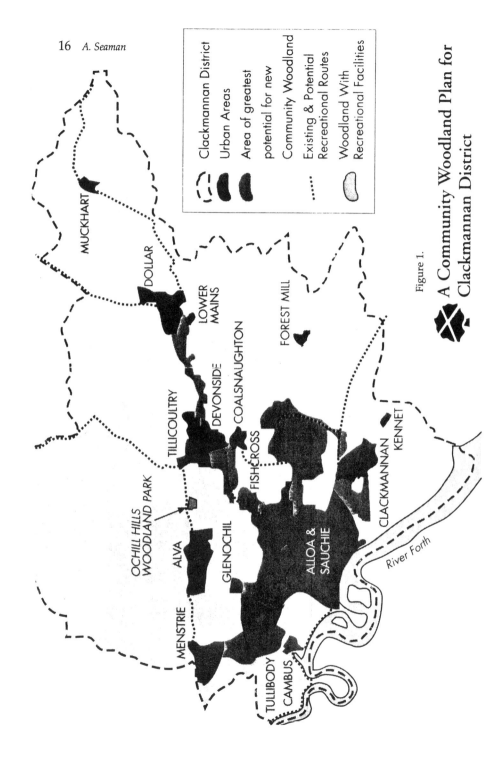

Figure 1.

A Community Woodland Plan for Clackmannan District

woodland design using specialist technical advice from foresters, conservation bodies and amenity organisations. Once a draft plan has been drawn up, it can be circulated to the groups initially contacted. Often it would be appropriate to organise a site visit where representatives of these organisations and any concerned individuals could see the site and comment on the proposals with the designer and owner. After the plan has been redrafted to take account of the community's ideas, the final step is to obtain formal community support and submit the scheme to the Forestry Authority for grant approval. As for any new planting scheme, grant aid will only be given after consultation with interested parties such as local councils and Scottish Natural Heritage. However, if all the ground work has been properly carried out, this should be a mere formality.

Site Survey

Design of any new wood should begin with a detailed site survey and this is especially important for community woodlands. Topographical features should be mapped to enable sensitive landscaping of the new wood ensuring that it fits properly into its surroundings. Special features to note include spurs, valleys, rocky outcrops, knolls and important viewpoints. Valuable wildlife features should also be recorded. These may include ponds and wet areas, existing trees and hedgerows, burns and ditches and areas of existing valuable ground vegetation. Also important to note are historical features such as registered archaeological sites, old dykes, agricultural ruins, and rig and furrow systems. Service facilities such as overhead electricity and telephone lines, mains water and gas pipes and rights of way should also be mapped. Appropriate matching of tree species to the site will require a soil survey which uses a combination of soil pits and identification of indicator plant species to produce a soil map. Finally, information on the local climate should be sought with rainfall and wind data being particularly important.

The final stage before detailed design commences is to identify other important management objectives for the wood. These may include provision of shelter for livestock, improving wildlife habitats, production of quality timber and catering for specialist recreations such as fishing or birdwatching.

Design Considerations

Once the background work has been completed, the first stage in the design process is usually to highlight the main access routes. These are usually designed to link important features such as gates, viewpoints and archaeological remains, while building on any existing rights of way. A variety of routes should be provided to cater for leisurely strollers and more ambitious walkers alike.

Consideration is then given to selecting species which will meet the objectives of management and grow well on the site. In an amenity wood this will usually involve a variety of trees and shrubs to provide a diversity of shape, size, colour and texture. It may be appropriate to select species with strong scents and interesting bark for blind members of the community to appreciate. Where creation of new wildlife habitats is important, species will often be restricted to those native to the area, whereas if shelter is a main objective, he wood will generally have a higher exotic conifer content.

The wood must then be landscaped to ensure that it fits into its surroundings. Detailed guidelines on forest landscape design have been produced by the Forestry Authority (1994) and all schemes must adhere to these if grant aid is to be sought. Based on contour maps, the survey map and photographs of the site, these guidelines involve giving consideration to "the spirit of the place" as well as to the main landscape themes of shape, scale, diversity, unity and visual force.

The incorporation of special features to aid and encourage community enjoyment of the wood should also be considered. For example, the provision of simple signs and information boards is usually a minimum requirement. If visitors are likely to arrive by car then adequate parking facilities should be provided. Other such features might include benches, picnic tables, litter bins, stiles, kissing gates, bird hides and, in larger woods, interpretation leaflets explaining interesting features in the wood. It may be appropriate to specifically provide a route accessible to wheelchairs. The Forestry Authority (1991) have produced guidelines for the use of these features in community woodlands (Figure 2) and, as for the landscape guidelines, these represent the standards required for grant approval.

In summary, woodland design is a matter of carefully balancing objectives and building on all the opportunities afforded by the site. Like designing a car or a house, the final outcome is a combination of technology and art. At one level the wood has to 'work', i.e. achieve its objectives, however there is also considerable scope for the designer to express his or her artistic flair. You can be sure that, given the same brief, no two designers will come up with quite the same end product!

Planting and Maintenance

Where possible, the local community should be involved in planting the wood. In addition to fostering a greater sense of responsibility and general interest in the wood, this provides an opportunity for learning about a whole host of woodland and nature subjects in a 'living laboratory'.

The use of plastic tree shelters should be avoided where possible. In addition to the expense involved, they are unsightly and, in proximity to urban centres, are often subject to vandalism. Instead potential mammal pests should be humanely controlled for the initial two or three years until the trees are adequately established. Reasons for pest control should be clearly explained to the local population although if they planted the trees, few are likely to dissent.

Ongoing maintenance will involve weed control for the first two or three

Signs and Information Boards

THESE will help people to get the most out of a woodland visit. They should be simple, robust and unobtrusive, and carefully positioned.

Car parking

CAR parking within the woodland should be reasonably spacious and informal, using a series of small, irregular parking bays.

Figure 2.

✤ Key Features of a Community Woodland

Woodland Edges

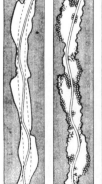
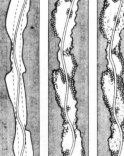
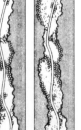

THE shapes, spaces and views from footpaths and other access routes will become more interesting by varying tree spacing, and using different species with different growth rates in irregular groups.

Access Routes

ROUTES for new footpaths should lead naturally from the entrance to a viewpoint, picnic area or other attraction, and where possible should build on those tracks which are already well used.

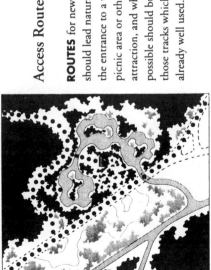

years. Pathways will need to be mown at least twice a year and each winter any dead trees should be replaced. Some local councils are willing to share the cost of regular maintenance such as grass cutting and bin emptying. Owners should be aware of their liabilities and ensure that gates, stiles and bridges etc are maintained in good working order. Perhaps one of the most important parts of the whole process is publicising the new wood to the community. An organised walk to explain the design and introduce the facilities may be appropriate (Figures 3 and 4). The promise of tea and cakes in the barn can often help boost the turnout! (Figure 5)

Conclusion

The owner's contract with the Forestry Authority requires the provision of public access for the first ten years. However, the woods themselves are virtually guaranteed in perpetuity and it is hoped that, with the provision of annual payments to help meet maintenance costs, owners will continue to encourage access into the foreseeable future.

References

Forestry Authority (1991) Community Woodland Design Guidelines; HMSO.
Forestry Authority (1993) The Clackmannan Community Woodland Plan.
Forestry Authority (1994) Forest Landscape Design Guidelines; HMSO.

More woods like Muckhart's are desirable – for information/discussion contact the author at 22 W. Burnside, Dollar FK14 7DP (0259) 743212.

Figure 3. The Muckhart community's guided walk.

Figure 4. Introducing the Muckhart Wood.

Figure 5. In the barn – after the walk/introduction.

ENVIRONMENTAL HISTORY: an emergent discipline

Assisted by Scottish Natural Heritage with foreword by Magnus Magnusson, this book for lay and learned alike is the first fruits of the newly founded Institute for Environmental History at St Andrews University. It challenges the reader's preconceptions and prejudices, and its readable authoritative chapters throw new light refreshingly on resource management in areas of farming, forestry and fishing, both in recent and distant times – matters today of urgent interest and controversy. All but one of the chapters were originally papers to the final conference of the Institute at Battleby in 1992. They include – Setting the scene: an overview of climatic change; Human impact on the prehistoric environment; Woodland history before 1850; Woodlands on Clanranald Estate – case study; Marginal agriculture; Environmental impact of sheep farming in the Highlands; Deer numbers in the Highlands since 1780; Midges in a changing Highland environment – are they only recent?; and a challenging look at Municipal agriculture in Sahel, southern edge of the Sahara desert – how local peoples can know better than experts how to treat fragile ecosystems.

Smout in his introduction emphasises the varied academic interests in this environmental history subject – always about human interaction with the natural world, but unlike economic history the main focus is not on economic growth and material enrichment in society but on the environmental impact of human exploitation of natural resources. The impact of agriculture on the history of soils and natural woodlands, the effect of hunting on animal stocks, and of grazing on nature vegetation. It is about the changes wrought by industry, forestry, mining, transport and urbanisation; natural phenomena effects – hurricanes, earthquakes ... with ancient times and societies as well as effects and conflicts of modern economic developments.

While slow to identify the subject as valid and distinctive, Scotland has seen the pioneering work last century of aspects of species and vegetation history by Harvie-Brown, and of human impact on fauna by Ritchie; in the 1950s, environmental archaeologists like Birks; and recent land use and forestry studies.

This book thus contributes strongly to the emergence of environmental history as a fledged discipline in Scotland.

L. Corbett

SCOTLAND SINCE PREHISTORY: Natural Change and Human Impact. editor T. C. Smout. 140pp. 1993. Scottish Cultural Press. ISBN 1-898218-03-X. £14.95

FORTH AREA BIRD REPORT 1993

C J Henty
University of Stirling

This report is compiled from a larger archive of records submitted to the local recorder under the national scheme organised by the Scottish Ornithologists Club. The area covered by the report comprises the Districts of Falkirk and Clackmannan together with Stirling District excluding Loch Lomondside and other parts of the Clyde drainage basin. Records from Carron Valley may be published both here and in the report on Clyde birds.

I am getting concerned that the separation of records into the four major areas is confusing the presentation of various items - in particular the first arrival dates of migrants would be more coherent on a regional basis. However, it is felt that any major change would be premature since the political/administrative boundaries are under review and the result is not yet clear. There has been a welcome increase in records from the inland part of Falkirk District.

There have been two recent major books covering the birds of our area. *Central Scotland (Land-Wildlife-People)*, 1993, published by Forth Naturalist and Historian, is in many ways an updated version of *The Stirling Region* (1974) and contains a chapter reviewing the status of the birds of Central Region. Also, the eagerly awaited account of the 1988-91 national survey of breeding birds, *The New Atlas of Breeding Birds in Britain and Ireland* (British Trust for Ornithology, 1993), has appeared and naturally the maps include results of local interest. However readers should be warned not to take at face value any apparent disappearances from the local 10 km squares compared with *1968-72 Atlas*. The recent survey was not so thorough so that many scarce or unobtrusive species have been overlooked, besides which it has become apparent that several sets of data went missing between observer and the BTO computer. Nevertheless, at a national level the *New Atlas* brings in novel methods of presentation and gives opportunity for repeated and enjoyable browsing.

The 1993 weather gave us overall temperature and rainfall that were close to average, although the monthly temperatures for the first half of the year were higher than normal this was evened up by a colder second half. However, as usual, these averages conceal much important short term variation. Thus early January was very wet and windy and after some mid-month snow had melted there was severe flooding. By contrast, February was consistently dull but strikingly dry until the last week brought rain and snow. Most of March was changeable until a late spell of snow and frost. April was generally unsettled and very wet until clear weather at the very end gave warm days and frosty nights which continued through early May. However, mid May was exceptionally cold with new snow on the hills, this led to unsettled weather with occasional warm days lasting through June and July.

August and September were much drier than usual but generally dull and lacking any extended sunny and warm spells. Early October was wet but then became calm and foggy with some severe frosts; this pattern stayed through most of November although the very end of the month brought rain and wind that continued into early December. The rest of December was unsettled but often cold with snow that lay only briefly on the low ground. There were thus no exceptional spells of weather that might be expected to affect birds markedly except that the cold of mid May could well have harmed breeding success.

The drake American Wigeon at Gartmorn Dam was officially accepted by the British Birds Rarities Committee and stayed well into 1993. Numbers of Blacktailed Godwits have continued to be consistently high around Grangemouth for much of the year and G.Owens counted an alltime record in April, the cessation of model plane flying at Skinflats has led to a much more consistent occupation of the pools. Once again the autumn passage of the scarcer waders was generally poor. There has been a welcome increase in Stonechat records suggesting that this species is at last recovering after years of low population. The record of a Lesser Whitethroat suggests that this species is attempting to colonise the region and it is worth investigating areas of dense deciduous scrub in May - in 1993 one sang from a bank of Hawthorn and Elder in Stirling. People wishing to become familiar with this and many other species might like to view a set of videotapes held by the SOC local branch - contact the secretary or Derek Jones at a meeting. Some comments on the abundance of common resident species have been made, quoting data on records per kilometre of transect or per hour; transects mean that birds have been recorded systematically along a particular route, counts usually being repeated on several dates. For less common species I can sometimes mention data in terms of the numbers of pairs or apparently occupied territories for particular locations. For many species the records sent in are very unrepresentative of their general distribution, this applies particularly to very common species or to those that are secretive or breed in inaccessible places. Readers can consult the Check List published in the *Forth Naturalist and Historian* vol 15, but in addition I have in this report put, after the species name, a coded summary of general distribution - which often apparently contradicts the detailed records that are published for the year.

B - Breeding status, widespread (in more than five 10 km squares)

b - "   " , local , scarce (in fewer than five 10 km squares)

W - Winter status, widespread or often in groups of more than ten.

w - "   " , local, scarce (local and usually fewer than ten in a group)

P - Passage (used when species is usually absent in winter, P or p used for widespread or local as in winter status)

S *or* s - a few species are present in summer but do not normally breed.

Thus *BW* would be appropriate for Robin, *B* for Swallow, *p* for Ruff and *SW* for Cormorant. No status letter is used if a species occurs less than every other year.

An asterix (*) in front of the species name means that all records received have been quoted.

For several species of waders and duck more information has been received than can be sensibly reported in full detail. In these cases I have mentioned the more striking individual records and summarised the rest for each month or half-month as the minimum number of birds that can reasonably account for the records, this means adding up the maximum numbers recorded for what I take to be distinct localities. These 'Area summaries' clearly have limitations, underestimating when an important locality has not been visited and overestimating if the same flock has been reported from two places that I have assumed to be separate; however, this is the best way of giving a more systematic description of the seasonal pattern of occurrence.

The following abbreviations have been used : AoT - apparently occupied territory, BoA - Bridge of Allan, c/n - clutch of n eggs, CP - Country Park, F - Female, GP - gravel pit, L. - Loch, NR - Nature Reserve, M - Male, Res - Reservoir, SP - summer plumage, WG - Wildlife Garden, Y - young.

This report has been compiled from records submitted by: K Anderson, M V Bell, H Bickerstaff, Birdline Scotland, A Blair, L T Bloomfield, W R Brackenridge, R A Broad, J Brown, W Brown, D M Bryant, J Calladine, M Callan, M Darling, H E M Dott, D Fairlamb, A Fairweather (AFw), A Falconer, Forest Enterprise, D Fotheringham, D Garratt, S Harley, S Hashim, B Hay, C J Henty, R Jones, A Knight, A Maciver (AMcI), J Mitchell, J Moss (JMs), A Murray, G Owens, D Orr-Ewing, D J Price, H Robb, P W Sandeman, S Sankey, J Sankey, R Shand, J Simpson, T D Smith, C&A Smout, A Stevenson (ASt), M Steward, P Stirling-Aird, A Summers, B R Thomson, D Thorogood, J Towill, M Trubridge, J Waley (JWy), J Wheeler, M Wilkinson.

Thanks are due to the Deputy Recorder, W.R.Brackenridge, for assistance and advice on records, to Dr S.J.Harrison for a copy of the Annual Climatological Bulletin (1993) and to Dr M.V.Bell for assessing the counts of geese.

SYSTEMATIC LIST

Codes - F and C indicate records from Falkirk and Clackmannan Districts, S and SWP those from one time Stirlingshire and south-west Perthshire parts of Stirling District.

RED-THROATED DIVER *Gavia stellata (b,w)*
F   1 Dunmore 24 Jan (DMB). 1 Blackness 6 Mar (CJH). 11 Skinflats 12 Dec (MVB).
SWP   Pair raised 2Y Loch E, 1 Loch G 23 Jun, 1 Loch A 14 Jul (MT). 1 Balquhidder 4 May (DJP). 4 Trossachs 4 Sep (AMcI).

BLACK-THROATED DIVER *Gavia arctica (b)*
F   2 Blackness 29 January (CJH).
SWP   2 pairs regularly on Loch A 29 Apr -11 Aug but no signs of breeding (MT).

LITTLE GREBE *Tachybaptus ruficollis (B,w)*
Certainly underrecorded in breeding season (Ed)
F   1 Kinneil 10 Oct (AB). 2 on Forth-Clyde canal Underwood
       (Bonnybridge) in Oct & Nov (AS).
C   10 pairs reared 14Y at Gartmorn (MC).
S   3 Craigforth 5 Dec (DT). 2 North Third Res 13 Nov (WRB).1 Airthrey
       28 January, 3 pairs in May, 5 by late July, probably 7Y raised from 4
       broods (MVB). 2 Cocksburn Res 2 May (CJH). 1 AoT Carron Valley
       Res 17 July (JM).
SWP   2 L.Venachar 1 & 28 Jan, 2 L.Dochart 31 Jan (CJH).

GREAT CRESTED GREBE *Podiceps cristatus (b,W)*
Forth estuary: 623 on 7 Feb (DMB).
F   Kinneil: 296 on 7 Feb, 200 on 7 Mar, 25 on 14 Apr, 3 on 9 May (CJH
       DT); 19 on 11 Jul, 73 on 25th & 110 on 28th; 265 on 29th Aug, 73 on 10
       Sep, 150 on 10 Oct & 213 on 31st (AB MVB HEMD CJH GO DT). 1
       Skinflats 31 Oct, 65 on 21 Nov & 2 on 28th (AB MVB). 55 Blackness 25
       January, 2 on 6 Mar (CJH). 5 Bo'ness 1 Sep (AMcI).
C   5 Gartmorn 17 Jan (CJH), 1 pair summered - no successful breeding
       (MC).
S   1 L.Coulter 14 Mar, pair on 18 April (CJH WRB). Carron Valley Res: 1
       on 2 Apr, 5 pairs 17 Jul (2 on nests & 1 with 1Y, 3Y finally reared), 5 on
       17 Oct (ad feeding large Y)(AFw AMcI JM DT).
SWP   11 Lake of Menteith 21 February, 4 on 14 Mar, 1 on 5 Dec (CJH DT).
       Pair Cambusmore 15 Mar to 3 Jun. Pair Blairdrummond 16 May to 8
       Jun (PWS). Pair L.Watston 11 Apr, with 2 juv 3 Sept (WRB PWS).

FULMAR *Fulmarus glacialis (p)*
F   3 ->E Skinflats (GO) & 1->W Blackness 9 Sep (WRB).
C   1 Cambus 21 March - under pylon,1-2 weeks dead (CJH).
S   1 ->E along scarp at Dumyat 18 Jun, appeared to fly up to a ledge on
       cliff and land (DMB).

GANNET *Sula bassana (p)*
F   Skinflats: 11 (9 imm, 1 2nd yr, 1 ad) on 9 Sep, 6 on 13th (GO). At
       Kinneil 1 imm on 29 Aug , 8 on 14 Sep (DMB); 1 imm Kinneil 15 Sep,
       stranded on mud with large gulls in attendance (DT).

CORMORANT *Phalacrocorax carbo (S,W)*
Forth Estuary: 696 on 18 Sep (DMB).
F   183 Carronmouth 5 Jan, 200 on 24 Dec (AB GO). 325 Skinflats 18 Sep
       & 628 on 28 Nov (MVB).
C   S.Alloa: 250 on 8 Jan, 300 on 1 Feb, 170 on 19 Feb ; 230 on 4 Sep & 300
       on 26th (DMB CJH PWS).
S   10 Carron Valley Res 19 Dec (DT).
SWP   4 Lake of Menteith 24 February (CJH). 3 over Thornhill 11 Sep (SS). 1
       L.Lubnaig 2 Apr & 10 Nov (DJP).1 L.Arklet 24 Apr (AMcI).

*SHAG *Phalacrocorax aristotelis (w)*
F   8 Airth shore 28 Nov (CJH). (Unusual party, probably others on river and birds found dead in 1994, Ed).
S   1 Airthrey 12 Oct - a very tame immature (CJH).

GREY HERON *Ardea cinerea (B,W)*
F   Skinflats max 17 on 29 Jun (AB GO). 4 Kinneil 3 Sep (GO). 10 Grangemouth 2 Nov (AMcI). 13 Kincardine Bridge 26 Dec (CJH). 36 Airth 15 Feb (PWS) & 42 Dunmore 14 Mar (AM).
SWP   9 Blairdrummond 7 Feb. 19 at heronry Lake of Menteith 21 Feb (CJH), 25 apparently occupied nests 23 Apr of which 17 found to have been used on 10 Jul (RAB).

*SPOONBILL *Platalea leucorodia (v)*
F   2 Skinflats 23 May. Heron size with long blackish legs and spatulate bills. Plumage primarily white, greyish white in places (no crests or yellowish on breast); one had small black tips to wings and the other a pinkish tip to bill, thus both 1st year birds. They were feeding in shallow saline pools with side to side sweeps of a slightly opened bill. When flying between pools the necks were extended and legs trailed and one bird carried a small fish. The birds were seen as close as 100m and last seen resting at the edge of a pool (DMB).

*CHILEAN FLAMINGO *Phoenicopterus chilensis*
F   2 Kinneil 25 Jul (DMB DT).

MUTE SWAN *Cygnus olor (B,W)*
F   Skinflats: more frequent than usual, max 13 on 7 Feb & 5 until 1 May (AB GO RS). 2 Kinneil 4 Jun & 1 on 26 Nov (GO). Pair with 3 juv Jupiter WG in mid Nov (WRB). 4 pairs + 5 imm on canal Castlecary-Bonnybridge 26 Nov (AS).
C   Cambus: 6 (4 imm) on 9 Jan, pair 29 Mar, on nest 24 Apr, with 4Y 14 Jun - 31 Aug, pair & 5 imm on 30 Oct (WRB CJH AM). 2 pairs on R.Devon Menstrie to Alva, with 1 imm on 27 Dec (BRT). Pair reared 6Y at Gartmorn Dam (MC).
S   32 (14 imm) by Forth at Taylorton 6 Apr (CJH). Pair Airthrey raised 5Y (SH). 8 Carron Valley Res 17 Oct (AM).
SWP   2 pair Blairdrummond Pool 7 Feb (1 chased away), 1 pair on 8 Jun; pair Lecropt 9 Feb (CJH PWS). 3 (1 imm) Kinbuck 30 Mar (BH).

WHOOPER SWAN *Cygnus cygnus (W)*
F   4 Airth 28 Mar (DT). 1 L.Ellrig 27 Sep (AM). Skinflats: 3 on 31 Jan, 5 on 7 Feb, 1 imm on 25 Apr. 7 on 17 Oct; 5 (flew off to SW) on 10 Nov & 17 on 14th (AB DMB HEMD GO). 20 in stubble W Carmuirs 2-24 Nov (AS).
C   19 Menstrie 25 & 26 Dec (BRT). Max 64 Gartmorn Dam 17 Mar (MC).
S   92 Kippen 23 Jan (DT). 5 L.Laggan 5 Feb, 10 Gargunnock 15 Mar (DT). 10 ->SW Airthrey 12 Feb & 13 ->SW on 19 Mar (DMB MVB). 27 North Third Res 20 Feb , 15 L.Coulter 14 Mar (WRB). 2 Carron Valley Res 19 Dec (DT).

SWP   32 L.Dochart 31 Jan, 40 on 14 Mar & 25 on 21st; 6 L.Venachar 28 Jan (DMB CJH C&AS). 5 (3 imm) L.Lubnaig 15 Feb-14 Mar, 3 imm L.Doine 14 April (DJP); 3 L.Voil 30 Mar (MT). 15 L.Achray 27 Feb, 6 Gartmore 30 Mar, 14 L.Katrine 21 Mar & 26 on 28th, 15 on 9 October; 4 L.Dhu 22 Oct (HR MT). 31 Lecropt 24 Jan (DT), 5 on 18 Dec, 7 on 23rd (MVB). 33 Thornhill 26 Jan & 27 on 28 Oct, 14 Bridge of Frew 18 Nov (SS MT); 18 ad East Garden 5 Dec, 17 Craigforth 4 Dec & 13 (1 Imm) on 5th (DMB DT).3 L.Doine17 Nov & L.Voil on 30th (DJP). Usual Drip Moss sites seem to have been deserted (Ed).

*BEWICK'S SWAN *Cygnus bewicki (w)*
S   2 Kippen (Fordhead) 23 Jan, with Whoopers (DT).
SWP   2 (with 3 Whoopers) L.Voil 30 Mar (AA).

PINK-FOOTED GOOSE *Anser brachyrhynchus (W)*
Report on whole area based on Central Scotland Goose Group and many other observers, summarised by MVB : Numbers in the Forth valley were low to average from Jan to Apr. Monthly maxima at the west end of the carse in the Lake of Menteith/Flanders Moss area were 3000 in early Jan, 4000 on 18 Feb and 2309 on 22 Mar (EB,SS). 1500 were still present at Loch Macanrie on 23 Apr (DT) but a complete count was not attempted that month. At the east end of the carse very few birds commuted from Strathallan, the 650 at Lecropt on 1 Jan and 2070 near Offers on 20 Mar were isolated flocks (MVB WRB DT). The last skein of spring was 50 ->W at Airthrey on 5 May (CJH). In autumn the first flock was 11 at Thornhill on 23 Sep and 3000 were there on 5 October (SS). 2440 roosted at Lake of Menteith on 17 Oct but numbers were much lower thereafter and none were found on the mid-November count; 360 near Thornhill on 13 Nov roosted elsewhere (MVB SS). In mid December an SNH/RSPB survey team found a minimum of 2100 birds in the area with at least 1500 roosting on Loch Rusky and 300 each at Flanders Moss and Lake of Menteith. Only small numbers used Loch Mahaick this autumn with 120 on 17 Oct and 600 on 13 Nov (MT). Very variable numbers fed at the east end of the carse at the year end with the largest flocks 3550 Lecropt on 23 Nov (following snow in Strathallan) and 2200 there on 26 Dec (MVB DMB WRB DT).

There was a large count of 4930 in the Kincardine-Clackmannan-Throsk area on 24 Jan (MVB DMB). Over 1000 remained into February with 1000 at Skinflats on 7th and 1100 at Alloa Inch on the 14th but the area was not checked thoroughly later in the spring. In autumn the first were 22 at Skinflats on 8 Oct and the roost held 2010 on 16 Oct and 2051 on 14 Nov. Later 1000 were at Plean on 24 Dec (DMB).

Away from the main areas small numbers were noted on the Slamannan plateau with 47 Shieldhill on 19 Jan and 50 Fannyside on 8 Oct (AMcI). 4 late birds were at Loch Katrine from 1-22 May (RAB).

BEAN GOOSE *Anser fabalis (W)*

F   150 Falkirk 16 Jan, stubble with Greylags (AMcI).

In the main area around Slamannan there were 63 on 16 Jan, 72 on the 17th (137 if two separately reported groups were different) & 50 on 30th (GO AMcI SS MW).First of autumn were 50 on 4 Oct rising to 131 on the 19th, max in Nov was 100 and in Dec 139 (SH AMcI GO JS SS TDS MW). The flock is very mobile (TDS) and it is apparent from the records that it splits up and reforms repeatedly (Ed).

S   42 Carron Valley Res 14 Oct, 93 on 16th & 84 on 17th (DF AMcI JS DT). *No strong reason to suppose these are a separate group to the main population in Falkirk District* (Ed).

*WHITE-FRONTED GOOSE *Anser albifrons (w)*

F   1 Slamannan 12 Dec (AMcI), 3 - Greenland form- on 19th (JS).

C   13 Alloa Inch 7 Feb - Greenland form (DMB).

GREYLAG GOOSE *Anser anser (b,W)*

Report on whole area based on Central Scotland Goose Group and many other observers, summarised by MVB : more than normal in Forth valley early in the year though, as usual, it was impossible to link feeding flocks with roosts. Most of the birds fed in the Gargunnock area where there were peaks of 2000 on 23 Jan and 1550 on 20 Mar. In autumn 530 were at Drip Moss on 24 Oct and 730 on 13 Nov when 90 were also at Thornhill (MVB MT DT).

Several hundred were present in the Skinflats to Alloa area at both ends of the year but in the absence of coordinated counts it was difficult to sort out duplication of flocks. 600 were at Alloa Inch on 31 Jan and smaller numbers remained at the Inches to April with 25 on 11th the last (DMB). The peak at Gartmorn was 210 on 10 Feb (MC). There were 190 at Skinflats on 24 Jan and 4 late birds over Grangemouth on 6 May (WRB). In autumn only low numbers were noted at Gartmorn (MC) but 260 were feeding at Clackmannan on 21 Nov with 445 there on 12 Dec and 100 Alloa Inch on 26 Dec. 170 roosted at Skinflats on 14 Nov (DMB).

In the Slamannan area 200-300 were present at both ends of the year with 340 Loch Ellrig on 8 Jan (CJH), 67 had returned by 20 Oct and 300 were present on 14 Nov (AMcI); 210 near Avonbridge 10 Nov & 349 on 11th (TDS) may also be this group. Away from the main feeding areas there were 100 Loch Coulter on 14 Nov (WRB) and 1 Loch Katrine 12 -18 May (RAB), whilst 47 flew high SW at Dollar on 24 Dec (CJH).

CANADA GOOSE Branta canadensis (b)

C   2 Tullibody Inch 23 & 25 Jul, 1 Aug & 4 Sep (DMB WB CJH).

SWP   9 Blairdrummond 7 Feb,2 pairs 23 Mar, pair with 2Y 6 Jun (DMB CJH PWS). 2 Kinbuck 30 Mar (BH). Pair Ashfield 6 Mar to 10 Apr (WRB).

BARNACLE GOOSE *Branta leucopsis (w)*
F   1 Kinneil 8,9 May (HEMD CJH GO). Skinflats: 172 on 21 Sep - flock
    rested at tideline then flew off high to SW (GO); 2 on 26 Sep & 21 on
    28th, 36 on 16 Oct, 11 on 13 Nov (AB DMB GO). 19 Kincardine Bridge
    19 Oct & 1 on 29th (MW DF). 1 L.Ellrig 16 Oct (SH).
C   2 Clackmannan 24 Jan. 1 Tullibody Inch 28 Jul & 2 on 26 Sept (DMB).
SWP Lecropt: 15 on 17 Jan, 1 on 1 Jan, 23 & 27 Nov, 12 & 18 Dec, 1 Thornhill
    30 Jan & 5 Dec; often with Pinkfeet (DMB MVB WRB DT).

SHELDUCK *Tadorna tadorna (b,W)*
Forth Estuary: 4283 on 18 Sep (DMB).
F   Skinflats: 500 on 8 Jan & 423 on 7 Feb. 1200 on 12 Sep, 1380 on 31 Oct,
    1050 on 28 Nov, 551 on 12 Dec (AB DMB MVB PWS). 165 on pools 4
    Apr, 200 on 8 May & 68 on 28 May (AB HEMD CJH). 5603 Kinneil 7
    Aug (DMB). Kinneil pool: 90 on 4 May & 70 on 8th (HEMD CJH),15
    ducklings on 1 June (GO), 4 broods (total 19) on 11 July plus 22 well
    grown young (DT). F killed by car Linlithgow Bridge in early June,
    brood of 9 taken to Jupiter WG, fledged in late July (WRB). 161
    Kennetpans 28 Nov (CJH).
C   20 Tullibody Inch 11 Apr, on 11 Jul 60 ad plus pair with 11 small Y, 54
    juvs on 1 Aug (DMB CJH). 2 Cambus 17 Apr to 22 May (SH).
SWP 2 Lake of Menteith 14 Mar (DT).

WIGEON *Anas penelope (b,W)*
Forth Estuary: 1634 on 12 Dec (DMB).
F   250 Kinneil 3 Jan, 86 on 6 Mar; 180 on 28 Nov, 223 on 5 Dec & 435 on
    31st (AB MVB GO DT). Last in spring Skinflats 25 Mar, 1st in autumn
    21 Sep (GO). 165 Carriden 12 Dec (DMB), 202 Kincardine Bridge 31
    Dec (MVB). 3 L.Ellrig 20 Feb (WRB).
C   Max 1260 Gartmorn 16 Jan (MC), 300 on 27 Feb. 205 Tullibody Inch 7
    Feb. 160 Alloa Inch 19 Feb, 180 on 14 Nov & 221 on 31 Dec (DMB MVB
    CJH). 3 Cambus 28 Aug (SH).
S   50 Carron Valley Res 11 Sep, 15 on 17 Oct (AMcI DO). 28 North Third
    Res & 4 L.Coulter 13 Nov (WRB).
SWP Cambusmore: 200 on 12 Feb, 500 on 10 Mar & 600 on 15th & 18th; pair
    on 3 Jun (PWS).
    10 L.Venachar 1 Jan (CJH). 2 Kirkton Glen 4 May (DJP). Pair Muir
    Dam 6 June (DMB).

*AMERICAN WIGEON *Anas americana*
C   M Gartmorn Dam 17 Jan, 6 & 14 Feb, present till March (WB MC AF
    CJH). *Presumably same bird that was seen in 1992* (Ed).

*GADWALL *Anas strepera (p)*
F   Skinflats: Pair on 26 Apr, 28 May & 11 June (AB GO).

TEAL *Anas crecca (B,W)*
Forth Estuary: 1437 on 7 Feb (DMB).
F   Kinneil: 260 on 3 Jan, 140 on 7 Mar, 170 on 4 Apr; 190 on 17 Oct (DT).

Skinflats:184 on 7 Feb, 80 on 18 Sep & 130 on 12 Dec (MVB). 545 Grangemouth 12 Dec (DMB). M Skinflats on 2 Jul & 4F on 8th - unusual late (or early ?,Ed) records (GO). 26 Parkfoot Marsh 23 Nov (AS).

C   208 Tullibody Inch 24 Jan , 180 on 7 Feb (DMB). 16 Devonmouth 14 Apr. Pair Cambus 25 Apr (SH). 6 Cambus 21 Aug (WRB). 50 Kennetpans 26 Dec (CJH). Max 180 Gartmorn Dam 18 Dec (MC).

S   Pair Lower Earlsburn Res 11 Apr (DT). F Airthrey 10 Dec (DMB) - *a rarity here !*(Ed)

SWP   20 L.Venachar 1 Jan (CJH). 30 Blairdrummond 23 Mar (PWS). Pair at 400m, Monachyle Glen 5 May (DJP). 38 Cromlix 14 Nov (WRB).

MALLARD *Anas platyrhynchos (B,W)*
Forth Estuary: 1006 on 12 Dec (DMB).

F   Skinflats: 260 on 24 Jan,195 on 7 Feb, 260 on 18 Sep, 334 on 12 Dec (MVB); Broods of 9 on 7 May & 5 on 18 Jul (GO). 200 Kinneil 3 Jan (DT). 27 L.Ellrig 20 Feb (WRB).

C   3 pairs nested Cambus (WRB). 10 (5Pr) on R.Devon at Alva 25 Dec (BRT).

S   47 L.Laggan 6 Feb (DT). 81 North Third Res 14 Nov (WRB). 654 Airthrey 17 Jan & 626 on 28th, 64 on 20 Mar; 550 on 19 August (MVB SH); probably 40 pairs nested, 1st brood 26 Mar but a bad breeding season with heavy losses of ducklings - Possibly food shortage ? (MVB).

SWP   170 L.Venachar 1 Jan, 160 Blairdrummond 7 Feb (CJH). 300 Cambusmore 12 Feb (PWS). Pair at 600m Kirkton Glen 17 Feb (DJP). 150 L.Watston 3 Sep, 62 Cromlix 14 Nov (WRB).

PINTAIL *Anas acuta (W)*
Forth Estuary: 99 on 7 Feb (DMB).

F   Skinflats: 65 on 24 Jan, 99 on 7 Feb, 82 on 7 Mar, few after 25 Mar and last a pair on 22 Apr. 9 on 15 Sept, 35 on 31 Oct, 55 on 28 Nov, 59 on 12 Dec & 69 on 31st (AB MVB GO DT). 59 Grangemouth 27 Nov (DMB). Kinneil: 11 on 5 Apr, 8 on 12th & 7 on 22nd; 8 on 29 Aug, 5 on 15 Sep, 14 on 17 Oct, M on 5 Dec (DMB GO CJH RS DT).

Area Summary

Jan	Feb	Mar	Apr	-	Aug	Sep	Oct	Nov	Dec
65	99	82	14		8	14	49	59	70

*GARGANEY *Anas querquedula (p)*
F   M Skinflats 4 to 7 May (AB WRB HEMD GO RS).

*SHOVELER *Anas clypeata (p)*
F   Pair Skinflats 9 May & M on 23rd; M on 3 Jun & pair on 11th, 2 on 16 Aug & 20 Sep (AB DMB GO). 1 Grangemouth 12 Sep; Kinneil: M on 1 Apr, 2 on 25 Jul & M on 12 Dec (DMB RS).

C   Pair Cambus 17 to 26 Apr (CJH SH), M on 30th (WB) ; 1 on 21 Aug (WRB). 5 (3M) Gartmorn 6 Sep & 11 Oct (WB MC).

POCHARD *Aythya ferina (W)*
F   M Grangemouth 25 Jul (DMB). 2 Skinflats 6 Feb (GO). 5M Kinneil 29 Aug (DMB).
C   30 Gartmorn 27 Feb, 54 on 23 Oct (WRB CJH).
S   M Airthrey 18 Mar (DMB). 6 North Third Res 14 Nov (WRB). 15 Carron Valley Res 11 Sep, 40 on 17 Oct & 19 on 19 Dec (AMcI GO DT).
SWP   20 L.Venachar 28 Jan (CJH). Loch Voil: 30 on 16 Jan, 14 on 15 Feb, 6 on 11 Mar; 5 on 12 Nov. 10 L.Lubnaig 10 Nov (DJP). Pair Blairdrummond 23 Mar (PWS).

TUFTED DUCK *Aythya fuligula (B,W)*
F   Pair Skinflats 16 Apr (GO). 1 Kinneil 22 Apr (RS).
C   3 Cambus 14 Apr (CJH), 6 on 19 May (AMcI), 2 on 29 Aug (SH). M on R.Devon at Alva 25 Dec (BRT).
S   61 Airthrey on 17 Jan, 45 on 20 Mar (SH). Pair L.Coulter 18 Apr (CJH). 10 Carron Valley Res 28 Jul, 38 on 11 Sep (CJH DO). 15 North Third Res 14 Nov (WRB).
SWP   Cambusmore: 20 on 12 Feb, 10 on 10 Mar, 6 pairs on 3 Jun (PWS). 22 Doune Ponds 23 Feb (WRB). Blairdrummond: 17 on 7 Feb, 40 on 23 Mar, 9 pairs on 16 May, 12 pairs on 8 Jun (CJH PWS). 20 Pairs L.Watston 11 April (PWS). 5 Argaty 24 Jun (PWS). 2 broods of 8Y & 2Y Ashfield in late Jul (WRB).

*SCAUP *Aythya marila (w)*
F   4 Bo'ness 24 Mar. Kinneil: 2 on 4 Jan & 23 Apr, 1 on 9 May, 3 on 7 Aug & 11 on 21st, 1 on 28 Nov, 5 & 19 Dec. Skinflats: 1F on 31 Jan; 5 to 7 Feb. (AB DMB MVB HEMD CJH GO DT).

*EIDER *Somateria mollissima (w)*
F   Blackness: 23 on 29 Jan, 10 on 6 Mar, 14 on 12 Apr (CJH). 2 Kinneil 6 Mar & 22 Apr, 1 on 26 Nov (AB GO RS). 4 Carronmouth 25 Apr (WRB). 2M Skinflats 2 May (DMB). Pair Carronmouth 12 Dec (MVB).

*LONG-TAILED DUCK *Clangula hyemalis (w)*
F   1 Skinflats 10 & 13 Oct (AB GO RS).

*COMMON SCOTER *Melanitta nigra (v/w)*
F   50 Kinneil, all F/imm, 28 Nov (DT); 4 Skinflats 31 Oct & 14 on 28th (AB DO GO).

GOLDENEYE *Bucephala clangula (W)*
Forth Estuary: 208 on 7 Feb (DMB).
F   9 Carriden 12 Dec (DMB). 11 Skinflats 7 Feb & 17 on 31 Oct (MVB), 9 on Pools 14 Mar & 5 on 28th (AB DT).
C   58 Gartmorn Dam 17 Jan (MC). 50 Alloa Inch 8 Jan & 68 on 24th, 54 Tullibody Inch 7 Feb (DMB PWS), 18 (11M) Cambus 20 Feb & 14 (9M) on 24th, 10 on 11 Apr & 5 on 14th; 20 on 26 Dec (CJH BRT).
S   5 Cambuskenneth 10 Feb (CJH). 3 Carron Valley Res 17 Oct (DT).
SWP   Lake of Menteith: 48 on 21 Feb, 36 on 15 Mar, 73 on 11 Apr (WRB CJH DT). 5 L.Dochart 31 Jan (CJH). 3 L.Voil 1 Mar (DJP). 25 L.Venachar 1

Jan & 19 on 28th; 12 Cambusmore 12 Feb & 10 (5 pairs) on 15 Mar; M Blairdrummond 7 Feb & 8 Jun (CJH PWS).

RED-BREASTED MERGANSER *Mergus serrator (B,W)*
Forth Estuary: 208 on 7 Feb (DMB).
F   Skinflats: 103 on 7 Feb, pair on 25 Mar; 130 on 31 Oct, 338 on 28 Nov & 112 on 12 Dec (MVB GO). 13 Kinneil 7 Feb & 59 on 7 Mar (DT). 135 Kennetpans 12 Dec (DMB). 15 Blackness 6 Mar (CJH).
C   Pair Cambus Pool 9 & 10 Apr, M on 26th (WB CJH SH).
SWP   Pair Blairdrummond 16 May & 11 Jun; F + 6Y L.Venachar 12 Jun (PWS). 2 Pairs Ashfield 24 Apr, F + 4 large Y late July (WRB). F + 6Y Dunblane 4 Aug (BH).

GOOSANDER *Mergus merganser (B,W)*
Forth Estuary: 27 on 12 Dec (DMB).
F   Skinflats: 17 on 5 Jan, 19 on 7 Feb, 16 F/imm on 25 Apr, 9 on 18 Sep, 46 on 28 Nov & 26 on 12 Dec (WRB MVB GO). 7 Skinflats Pools 28 Mar, 16 on 13 Apr & 22 on 18th, 9 on 5 May; 5 on 28 & 30 Sep, 7 on 10 Oct (AB GO DT). 4 Carronshore 19 May & 27 Dec (AB).
C   6 Tullibody Inch 19 Feb (CJH). 5 Cambus Pool 19 May (AMcI). 7 Cambus 31 Oct (WB) & 4 on 26 Dec (BRT).
S   7 L.Laggan 6 Feb (DT). 4 Carron Valley Res 17 Oct, 8 (4M) Cambuskenneth 28 Oct (CJH AMcI).
SWP   3 L.Voil 5 Jan & 2 on 1 Mar (DJP). F L.Arklet 21 Apr (AMcI). 4 Cambusmore 10 Mar (PWS). Pair Goodie Water 10 & 12 Apr (JS). 1 Blairdrummond 7 Feb & 23 Mar, pair on 16 May (CJH PWS). 2 Lake of Menteith 21 Feb, 3 (2M) on 21 Apr (CJH AMcI). Max 5 Ashfield Nov-Dec (WRB). Pair on R.Allan Dunblane Jan & Apr, 4F on 22 Oct; 10 between there and BoA on 26 Oct, 4 on 7 Nov & 4 (1M) on 4 Dec (BH). F + 16 Y on R.Teith 11 Jun (PWS).

*RUDDY DUCK *Oxyura jamaicensis (b)*
SWP   2 pairs L.Watston 11 Apr, 7 (4M) on 7 Jun, 2 F/imm on 3 Sep (WRB DMB PWS). 4F Doune Ponds 18 Sep (WRB).

HEN HARRIER *Circus cyaneus (b?,W)*
F   Slamannan area: 1 on 19 Nov, 7 & 18 Dec (AMcI TDS); 3 on 19 Dec (JS).
C   1 Gartmorn 7 Jan (DT).
S   M Cambuskenneth 25 Jan (CJH). 1 Gargunnock 5 Dec; M Carron Valley Res 16 Aug, 1 ringtail Aug-Nov (AFw) & 1 on 12 & 19 Dec (WRB DT).
SWP   Thornhill-Flanders Moss: 2 on 26 Jan, 1 on 7 Feb & M on 11th, M on 27 Mar, M 16 & 24 Sep, 8 Oct, M&F on 9 Oct (DO JS SS). 1 Sheriffmuir 10 Oct; M Blairdrummond 5 Dec (MVB). None seen Braes of Doune, persecution suspected (WRB).

GOSHAWK *Accipiter gentilis*
F   F Kinneil 1 May (RS).
SWP   1 with Raven over Ashfield 14 Nov (WRB).

SPARROWHAWK *Accipiter nisus (B,W)*
F   Through year at Jupiter WG (WRB). Pair raised 3Y Skinflats (AB DMB GO). Used nest Howierigg (ASt). 1 Dunmore 15 Mar, Falkirk 28 Jun & 4 Sep, Bo'ness 18 Jul, Slamannan 14 & 19 Nov & 12 Dec (AMcI).
C   Pairs bred Wood Hill (3Y), Birkhill (4Y), Gartmornhill (3Y) (MC). 1 Cambus 23 Jul (WB). F flushed from remains of Dunlin at Tullibody Inch 19 Oct (CJH).
S   In Stirling garden M on 8 & 10 Apr (once on bird table); F caught Blackbird 18 July, chased by corvids 21 & 23 Oct (RJ).
SWP   2 L.Ard Forest 23 May (CJH). Through year at Dunblane, chased by Carrion Crows in Jan (BH).

BUZZARD *Buteo buteo (B,W)*
F   1 ->E Skinflats 27 Feb (AB). 1 Kinnaird Jan-Mar & Nov - Dec (WRB DT). 4 Dunmore 14 Mar & 2 on 15th (AMcI). 2 Letham in Mar (per RAB).
C   1 Gartmorn 17 Jan (CJH). 1 Forestmill 24 Apr (RS). 1 Alva Glen 26 Jun (WRB). Pair reared 2Y Dollar (MC).
S   3 AoT Carron Valley Forest (AFw). Pair Plean 10 Apr, 1 on 3 Sep & 17 Oct; 1 Stirling on 16 Nov (DT). 1 BoA 11 Oct - watched flying WSW for 8 km (CJH). 2 pairs diving at each other Cocksburn Res 2 May, 1 bird 24 Oct (CJH); 5 pairs Airthrey - Doune in summer (DMB).
SWP   4 AoT in May-Jun in 5 sq km, L.Ard Forest (CJH). Blairdrummond: 4 pairs + 1 on 31 Mar. 6 Hill of Row 7 Feb. Lake of Menteith: 3 AoT 21 Feb + another on 2 Apr (CJH). Thornhill: 13 Jan (pair), 27 Mar, 13 Apr, 20 Dec (CJH SS). 1 Flanders Moss 7 Feb (SS). Braes of Doune: 5 AoT Cambusbeg - Argaty Feb-Apr (CJH PWS). 2 AoT Kilbryde 4 Apr. 3 Keir 3 Jan (WRB). 1 Dunblane 4 Apr & 27 Sep. 3 Cromlix 17 Feb (BH). At Balquhidder Apr-Nov (DJP).

GOLDEN EAGLE *Aquila chrysaetos (b,w)*
SWP   Overall: 9 ranges checked, 7 pairs & single bird, 3 successful pairs raised 3 Y (PS-A). 2 Stronachlachar 21 Apr (AMcI).2 Balquhidder Apr-Oct (DJP). 2 Ben Ledi (1 ad, 1 sub-ad) & 1 Meall Cala 28 Nov (WRB).

OSPREY *Pandion haliaetus (p)*
C   1 Gartmorn Dam 3 & 7 Sep (MC).
SWP   First seen Trossachs 31 Mar (DT), 1 Gargunnock early August, 1 Callander 17 Aug (per MT).

KESTREL *Falco tinnunculus (B,W)*
7 regularly hunting along M9 Keir- Grangemouth (WRB), 8 on 8 Oct (BH).
F   M at Jupiter WG till late March, when nest box erected; 5 Denny quarry (? family) in July (per WRB).
C   Bred Woodhill (3Y), Fishcross (3-4Y), Tillicoultry 2Y, Alva Glen 2Y (MC).
S   1 chased by Peregrine at Blairlogie7 May (DRT).

*MERLIN *Falco columbarius (b?,w)*
F   1 Slamannan 11 Dec (TDS).
C   1 Forestmill14 Feb (DT). 1 Yetts of Muckhart 15 Oct (RJ).
S   1 Airthrey 1 Feb (DMB).
SWP   1 Ashfield 13 Nov (WRB). 1 Thornhill 27 Dec (CJH).

PEREGRINE *Falco peregrinus (B,W)*
F   Kinneil: Pair on 13 Jun; 1 on 10 Aug, 9 Sep, 10 Oct (AB GO RS DT), on 15 Sep one forced a Blacktailed Godwit down into rough water on the estuary then flew on (DT). 1 Skinflats 5 Feb, 12 & 29 Aug, pair on 11 Nov (AB GO RS). 1 Grangemouth 2 Nov (AMcI).
C   3 pairs raised 7Y (PS-A). 2 swooped on Woodpigeons at Glenochil 25 Dec. 1 Cambus 26 Dec, 1 imm at Gogar on 30th landed in field disturbing Starlings & thrushes (BRT).
S   1 Stirling 17 Mar (DJP).
SWP   16 ranges checked, 12 pairs & 3 single birds; 6 successful pairs reared at least 12 Y (PS-A). 1 Thornhill 9 Apr, 27 Dec (CJH JS). M Blairdrummond 31 Mar (CJH).

RED GROUSE *Lagopus lagopus (B,W)*
SWP   Few on Braes Doune above Cromlix 17 Apr (WRB). 2 Sheriffmuir 23 & 31Jan (WRB RS).

*PTARMIGAN *Lagopus mutus (b,w)*
SWP   2 Glen Gyle 3 Jan (PWS). 1 at 800m Kirkton Glen 4 May (DJP).

BLACK GROUSE *Tetrao tetrix (B,W)*
S   M & 2 F Carron Valley (W) in May (AFw).
SWP   Lek at Ardeonaig (L.Tay): 6 on 23 Feb, 13 (1F) on 8 May. 1 Callendar, dead under wires, 26 Feb (PWS). 3M Lake of Menteith 5 Aug (DT). 4M Glen Casaig 28 Nov (WRB). Max 2 Kirkton & Monachyle Glens Mar-Nov (DJP).

*CAPERCAILLIE *Tetrao urogallus (b,w)*
SWP   F L.Ard Forest 31 Jul (CJH).

GREY PARTRIDGE *Perdix perdix (B,W)*
F   Through year at Skinflats, max 16 on 28 Sep (AB). 10 on saltmarsh S.Alloa 1 Feb (PWS). 13 on saltmarsh Powfoulis 24 Jan (MVB). 7 Kinneil 7 Feb (DT). 1 Slamannan 6 Mar & 2 Dunmore 27 Jun (AMcI). 4 Bonnybridge 8 Nov (AS).
C   2 Cambus 25 & 26 Apr, 7 on 26 Dec (SH BRT). Autumn coveys of 12 Gartmorn & 14 Cambus (MC). 10 by Devon, Dollar, 24 Dec (CJH).
SWP   6 Lecropt 17 Feb (CJH). 2 pairs Ashfield Nov-Dec (WRB). In stubble: 14 Drip Moss 22 Nov, 18 Thornhill 20 Dec (CJH).

*QUAIL *Coturnix coturnix*
F   1 calling Bonnybridge 16 Jul (ASt).

PHEASANT *Phasanias colchicus (B,W)*
S   several reports from gardens in Stirling (RJ et al).

*WATER RAIL Rallus aquaticus (w)
F   1 Bonny Marsh 27 Oct (AS).
C   5 Tullibody Inch 4 Sep (DMB). 1 Cambus 30 Oct & 2 Nov (CJH).

MOORHEN Gallinula chloropus (B,W)
S   51 Airthrey 20 Feb & 22 on 11 Nov, 16 territories but only 7Y fledged
        due to Mink (MVB SH).

COOT Fulica atra (B,W)
F   Pair raised 3Y Skinflats (GO). 1 Kinneil 8 Aug (DT).
S   Pair L.Coulter 14 Mar (WRB). 81 Airthrey 17 Jan, 20 pairs but only 4Y
        fledged due to Mink (MVB SH).
C   8 Cambus Pool 20 Feb, 3 nests 14 Apr (CJH). 1 on Forth at Alloa Inch
        4 Sep; 1 Kennetpans 27 Nov - left cover weakly to Forth (DMB).
SWP   379 Lake of Menteith 5 Dec (DT).

OYSTERCATCHER Haematopus ostralegus (B,W)
804 Forth estuary 24 Jan (DMB).
F   175 Kinneil 3 Jan, 115 on 29 Aug (DMB DT). Skinflats: 83 on 7 Feb, 90
        on 5 May & 64 on 4 Aug, 65 on 28 Nov & 67 on 12 Dec (AB MVB). 63
        Higgins Neuk 6 Mar (CJH).
C   Nightflighting Menstrie 10 Feb, several on 11th (BRT). 60 Tullibody
        Inch 19 Feb, 20 on 23 July; 120 Cambus 15 May & 63 on 26th (CJH).
S   2 Craigforth 30 Jan, 200 on 17 Feb; 150 Cambuskenneth 10 Feb;
        nightflighting Stirling 6 Feb, BoA on 9th (WRB CJH DT). Pair bred on
        Stirling University roof, carried worms to young.
SWP   3 Lecropt 17 Jan (DMB). 30 Cambusmore on 12 Feb, 200 on 10 Mar &
        600 on 15th. Blairdrummond: 80 on 31 Mar, 50 on 16 & 24 May, 8 Jun
        (PWS). 50 L.Watston 11 Apr, 50 Argaty 20 Apr, 18 & 23 May,100 on 24
        Jun (PWS). Nightflighting Dunblane 7 Feb (MVB). Ashfield-Kinbuck:
        2 on 1 Feb, 40 on 22 Mar & 200 on 30th, 105 on 11 Apr, 10 on 27 May
        (WRB BH). 1 nested by edge of A9 at Keir (WRB).

RINGED PLOVER Charadrius hiaticula (b,W)
66 Forth estuary 18 Sep (DMB).
F   Skinflats: 4 on 14 Mar, 30 on 30 May, 20 on 4 Jun & 5 on 26th, 12 on 18
        Sep & 31 Oct (AB MVB GO). 9 Kinneil 3 Sep (DT). Heard at opencast
        site Howierig 19 Jul (ASt).
S   Pair + 1 Lower Earlsburn Res 11 Apr (DT).
SWP   2 Argaty 20 Apr & 1 on 23 May; 1 Blairdrummond 24 May; 2 L.Tay (W)
        23 Jun (PWS).

*DOTTEREL Charadrius morinellus
C   1 Ochils 20 Jun (MC).

GOLDEN PLOVER Pluvialis apricaria (B,W)
609 Forth estuary 18 Sep (DMB).
F   Skinflats: 40 on 7 Feb; 10 on 3 Sep, 70 on 4th, 105 on 18th & 100 on 20th
        & 28th, 570 on 31 Oct, 51 on 11 Nov (AB DMB MVB GO DT). 130
        Slamannan 16 Oct (AMcI), 35 on 10 Nov, 14 on 22nd (DO TDS). 11

Avonbridge 15 Nov (AMcI).

SWP   1 Flanders Moss on 27 Mar, 10 ->E Thornhill 9 Apr (SS). 4 Ardeonaig 2 Jun (PWS).

GREY PLOVER *Pluvialis squatarola (W)*
88 Forth estuary 18 Sep (DMB).

F   Skinflats: 17 on 18 Jan, 5 on 30 May; 1 on 2 Sep, 50 on 18 & 20 Sep & 225 on 28th, 200 on 15 Oct, 181 on 17th, 88 on 30th & 73 on 31st, 13 on 2 Nov (AB DMB MVB AMcI GO). 1 in SP Kinneil 7 Aug, 2 on 21st, 61 on 17 Oct (DMB MVB DT).

C   4 Tullibody Inch 26 Sep (DMB) - *scarce so far up estuary* (Ed)..

LAPWING *Vanellus vanellus (B,W)*
3692 Forth estuary 18 Sep (DMB).

F   25 Darnrig Moss 20 Feb (WRB). 50 Slammannan 14 Nov (AMcI). Kinneil: 300 on 3 Jan, 180 on 15 Sep, 400 on 2 Oct, 8 Pairs on 23 May (DMB DO DT). Skinflats: 300 on 7 Feb, 590 on 18 Sep, 450 on 31 Oct, 500 on 2 Nov & 625 on 12 Dec (MVB AMcI). 100 Skinflats Pools on 18 Jul (AB), 2 pairs (WRB).

C   750 Cambus 9 Jan, 700 on 20 Feb, 107 on 26 Dec; 3 AoT on 10 May; 2 AoT Craigrie 21 Mar (WRB CJH BRT). Tullibody Inch: 360 on 19 Feb, 400 on 23 Jul, 1320 on 1 Aug & 2000 on 26 Sep (DMB CJH).

S   8 pairs Bandeath 8 May (DMB). 200 Kincardine Bridge 8 Jan, 500 S.Alloa 1 Feb & 500 Airth on 15th (PWS).

SWP   2 pairs Bows, fewer at Ashfield and poor success due to removal of rushes (WRB). 10 Cambusmore 12 Feb, 50 on 10 Mar & 200 on 15th. 50 Argaty 10 Mar & 20 on 24 Jun. 20 Blairdrummond 8 Jun (PWS).

KNOT *Calidris canutus (W)*
7240 Forth estuary 12 Dec (DMB).

F   Kinneil: 1200 on 3 Jan; 1 (imm) on 8 Aug & 20 on 21st, 10 on 12 Sep, 3000 on 27 Nov, 4460 on 12 Dec & 4700 on 31st (DMB MVB DT). Skinflats: 200 on 8 Jan, 7 on 16 May; 3 on 23 Aug, 11 on 18 Sep, 200 (on pools) 15 Oct, 650 on 17th, 1320 on 31st (AB DMB MVB PWS).

C   1 Cambus 9 Aug (WB).

*SANDERLING *Calidris alba*
F   1 Skinflats 23 Apr (GO).

*LITTLE STINT *Calidris minuta (p)*
F   1 (imm) Skinflats 1 Sep , 1 on 20th (GO RS). 1 Kinneil 12 Sep (DMB).

CURLEW SANDPIPER *Calidris ferruginea (p)*
F   Skinflats: 1 on 7 May, 1 (ad in moult) Skinflats 6-19 Aug, 4 on 25th & 2 on 28th; 1 imm on 2 Sep, 1 on 12th, 3 on 20th, 8 on 21st, 1 on 28th; 2 on 17 Oct (AB DMB GO RS). Kinneil: 9 on 3 Sep, 2 on 12th & 1 on 26th (DMB GO DT).

Area Summary (half monthly)

May	-	Aug	Sep	Oct
1	0	1 4	10 9	0 2

DUNLIN *Calidris alpina (b?,W)*
5002 Forth estuary 12 Dec (DMB).
F   Kinneil: 250 on 3 Sep, 1200 on 27 Nov & 600 (several birds oiled) on 28th, 1355 on 12 Dec, 4550 on 31 Dec (DMB MVB DT). 4380 Grangemouth 27 Nov (DMB). 500 Higgins Neuk 17 Oct (CJH). Skinflats: 1700 on 7 Feb; 1 on 26 June, 4 from 3 Jul (GO), 450 18 Sep, 16 on 31 Oct, 600 on 2 Nov, 3800 on 28 Nov, 2940 on 12 Dec (MVB AMcI).
C   66 Tullibody Inch 19 Feb (CJH).

RUFF *Philomachus pugnax (p)*
F   Kinneil: 1 on 2, 8 & 19 Aug; 3 on 3 Sep & 1 on 12th (DMB GO RS). Skinflats: 1 on 25 & 27 Apr (GO), 1 on 8, 12 & 15 Aug, 2 on 22 Aug, 2 on 15 Sep (AB AF DT).
C   4 Cambus 15 Aug, 2 on 18th, 7 on 28th (WB CJH SH).
    Area Summary (half monthly)

Apr	-	Aug		Sep	
0	1	6	10	5	0

JACK SNIPE *Lymnocryptes minimus (w)*
F   Kinneil: 6 on 19 Jan, 3 on 20th & 2 on 30th, 2 on 7 Feb; 5 on 13 Oct & 6 on 31st (MD JMs GO RS DT). 1 Skinflats 21 Nov (AB).
C   1 Kennetpans 3 Nov (CJH).

SNIPE·*Gallinago gallinago (B,W)*
F   Kinneil: 25 on 15 Sep, 60 on 17 Oct (DT). 7 Skinflats 19 Aug, 5 on 21 Nov (AB GO). 1 Jupiter WG Feb-Mar (WRB). 32 Parkfoot Marsh 3 Nov & 15 on 23rd, 16 on 7 Dec (AS).
C   Kennetpans: 41 on 24 Oct, 25 on 3 Nov, 21 on 12 Dec & 5 on 26th (DMB CJH). 1 AoT Cambus 10 Apr (CJH); 24 on 14 Aug & 20 on 18th (WB SH). 5 Tullibody Inch 26 Sep (DMB).
SWP   1 AoT Bows 17 Apr (WRB).

WOODCOCK *Scolopax rusticola (B,W)*
F   1 over Grangemouth (heavy snow) 22 Dec (WRB). 1 Howierigg 19 Jul & 2 on 22 Nov (AS ASt).
C   1 Sheardale 21 Nov (DT).
SWP   1 Thornhill 1 & 27 Feb (SS). 2 with Y Ardeonaig 15 May (PWS).

BLACK-TAILED GODWIT *Limosa limosa (W)*
F   Kinneil: 30 in Jan, 37 through Feb and early Mar, 22 on 27 Mar, 14 on 1 April & 17 on 22nd, 20 on 25 Jul, 38 on 29 Aug, 21 on 3 Sep & 7 on 26th, max 34 through Sep & Oct, 24 on 5 Dec & 10 on 19th (AB DMB MVB JC JMs GO RS DT). Skinflats: 2 on 5 Jan, 1 on 12 Feb, 8 on 25 Mar & 30 on 28th; 134 on 23 Apr; max 19 in May; 1 on 8 & 26 Jun; 2 on 3 Jul & 5 on 29th, 15 on 7 Aug, 7 on 22 Aug & 30 Sep; (AB WRB DMB AF CJH DO GO RS). 4 Grangeburn 5 Oct (RS). A bird at Skinflats 5 & 9 May had red & orange rings on right and green & yellow rings on left leg (AB). GO's count of 134 at Skinflats in April is a record and coincides with unusual numbers at Cambus.

C   Cambus: 36 on 21 Apr, 19 (12 in BP) on 15 May, 5 on 9 Aug (WB CJH).
Area Summary (half monthly) (Area = whole Region)

	Jan	Feb	Mar	Apr	May	Jun	Jul	Aug	Sep	Oct	Nov	Dec
Knnl	29 30	37 17	36 22	14 17	0 0	0 0	0 20	12 38	21 7	33 34	0 32	24 10
Sknf	2 0	1 0	0 30	34 134	19 16	1 1	2 5	15 7	4 7	0 0	0 0	0 0
Area	31 30	38 17	36 52	48 187	19 35	1 1	2 25	32 45	25 14	37 34	0 32	24 10

BAR-TAILED GODWIT *Limosa lapponica (W)*
402 Forth estuary 24 Jan (DMB).
F   Kinneil: 120 on 3 Jan, 70 on 28 Nov, 170 on 5 Dec, 230 on 12th, 100 on 19th (AB DMB DT). Skinflats: 4 on 7 Feb, on Pools - 1 on 9 & 12 May & 3 on 21st, 1 on 25 Jul & 6 on 6 Aug (AB MVB GO).

WHIMBREL *Numenius phaeopus (p)*
F   Skinflats: 5 on 7 May (left W), 4 on 8th (left N), 1 on 15th & 30th, 1 on 4 Jun; 1 on 14-19 Jul & 5 on 24th, 5 on 1 Aug & 2 on 5th, last on 19th (AB GO RS). Kinneil: 3 on 25 Jul & 1 on 28th, 1 on 10 Aug, 1 on 19th & 2 on 21st. 1 on 10 Sept (AB DMB RS DT).
C   2 Tullibody Inch 23 Jul & 3 on 21 Aug (DMB CJH). 1 Cambus 17 Aug (SH).
S   1 Bandeath 8 May (DMB).
SWP   2 Thornhill 25 Jul (SS).
Area Summary (half monthly)

May	Jun	Jul	Aug	Sep
6 1	1 0	1 12	5 6	1 0

CURLEW *Numenius arquata (B,W)*
1807 Forth estuary 24 Jan (DMB).
F   Kinneil: 300 on 25 Jul, 600 on 29 Aug, 630 on 12 Sep & 250 on 15th (DMB DT). 470 Grangemouth 21 Aug (MVB). Skinflats: 375 on 24 Jan, 512 on 7 Feb, 194 on 18 Sep, 187 on 31 Oct, 300 on 19 Dec (MVB AMcI). 50 by M9 Kinnaird early Dec, 10 flying inland there 11 Jul. 20 Dunmore 15 Feb, 40 on 14 Mar & 109 on 28 Nov (WRB CJH AMcI PWS). 2 AoT Maddiston 26 Apr (AMcI).
C   153 Kennetpans 24 Oct & 190 on 26 Dec. 40 Cambus 21 Mar; 60 Tullibody Inch 1 Apr & 30 on 23 Jul (DMB CJH).
S   130 Stirling ring-road early March & 50 at end Oct (BRT).
SWP   2 Cambusmore 12 Feb, 10 on 10 Mar & 50 on 15th (PWS). Braes of Doune: 4 AoT Bows, 2 AoT Cromlix (WRB).

*SPOTTED REDSHANK *Tringa erythropus (p)*
F   1 Skinflats 1, 2 , 4, 12 & 18th Aug, 2 on 16th & 23rd, 3 on 19th & 22nd; 1 on 13 Sep & 2 on 15th; 1 on 2 Oct & 2 Dec (AB DO GO RS AF). 1 Kinneil 31 Oct (MD).
C   1 Kennetpans 24 Oct (DMB).

REDSHANK *Tringa totanus (B,W)*
2708 Forth estuary 18 Sep (DMB).
F   Skinflats: 940 on 21 Jan, 920 on 7 Feb, 350 on 4 Apr; 1005 on 18 Sep, 1140 on 31 Oct, 1100 on 28 Nov, 760 on 12 Dec (AB MVB). 150 Higgins

Neuk 25 Apr (WRB). 560 Kinneil 12 Apr, 1010 on 29 Aug; 500 Grangemouth 2 Nov & 2160 on 29th (DMB CJH AMcI). 70 Blackness 12 Apr . 100 Airth 15 Feb & 14 displaying there on 2 Apr (CJH PWS).
C   2 Cambus17 Apr - 3 May, 1 on 22 May (SH).
SWP   2 AoT Bows; 40 Kinbuck 30 Mar,1 AoT Ashfield (WRB BH).

GREENSHANK *Tringa nebularia (p)*
F   Skinflats: 1 on 28 Apr, 8&9 May; 1st of autumn 1 Jul, regularly from 15 Jul to 26 Sep, max 5 on 5 & 7 Aug & 3 on 10th & 18th, last 1 on 13 Oct (AB DMB HB GO RS). Kinneil: from 25 Jul to 10 Sep, max 3 on 7 Aug & 4 on 8th, last on 13 Oct (DMB JMs GO RS DT). 1 Higgins Neuk 29 Oct (DF).
C   2 Cambus 10 Apr flew off N (CJH). At Cambus 22 Jul to 21 Sep, max 3 on 13 Aug (1 with squeaky call) & 2 on 15th who had a prolonged and vigorous aggressive encounter (WB WRB CJH SH). 1 Alloa Inch 26 Sep (DMB).
Area Summary (half monthly)

Apr	-	Jul	Aug	Sep	Oct
2 0		1 3	12 4	4 2	2 1

*GREEN SANDPIPER *Tringa ochropus (p)*
F   Kinneil: 1 on 2, 3 & 8 Aug, 3 Sep (GO RS DT). Skinflats: 1 on 1, 5, 7,10 & 22 Aug, 2 on 4th & 6th (AB DMB AF GO RS).
C   1 Cambus 22 & 25 Jul, 2 & 21 Aug, 4 Sep (WB DMB CJH SH).
Area Summary (half monthly)

Jul	Aug	Sep
0 1	5 2	2 0

*WOOD SANDPIPER *Tringa glareola (p)*
F   1 Skinflats 1 Aug (RS).

COMMON SANDPIPER *Tringa hypoleucos (B)*
F   1 Kinneil 8 May, 1 on 25 Jul, 3 on 1 Sep (DMB GO DT). Skinflats: 1st of autumn 2 on 14 Jul to 7 Aug, max 3 on 1 Aug (AB GO).
C   1st Cambus 17 Apr, Gartmorn Dam 20 Apr (MC SH). 2 Tullibody Inch 23 Jul (CJH).
S   1 Lower Earlsburn Res 11 Apr (DT).
SWP 1st L.Ard 17 Apr (MT). Pair Ashfield, 1 Barbush 18 Aug (WRB).
Area autumn totals, estuary :

	Jul	Aug	Sep
	2 5	3 0	3 0

TURNSTONE *Arenaria interpres (W)*
68 Forth estuary 12 Dec (DMB).
F   1 Carronmouth 5 Jan. 1 Kinneil 25 Jul & 2 on 26 Nov (GO DT).

*POMARINE SKUA *Stercorarius pomarinus (p)*
F   1 imm Skinflats 2 & 31 Oct (GO).

*ARCTIC SKUA *Stercorarius parasiticus (p)*
F   1 ->E Skinflats 9 Sep, 2 on 20th, last 1 on 17 Oct. 1 Kinneil 8 Aug & 12 Sep (AB DMB GO DT).

*LITTLE GULL *Larus minutus (p)*
F 1 lst summer Skinflats 22 May to 8 June (AB DMB GO RS). 1 adult Skinflats 15 August (AB).

BLACK-HEADED GULL *Larus ridibundus (B,W)*
F Skinflats: 52 lst summer on 28 May, lst juv on 30 Jun (CJH GO); 200 on 20 Sep (AB). Several oiled birds at Kinneil 28 Nov (DT).
C 2000 on flooded pasture Cambus 30 Jan; 2500 Gartmorn 23 Oct (CJH).
SWP 900 on flooded pasture Blairdrummond 31 Mar (CJH), 1000 Argaty 10 Mar, 500 on 20 Apr & 300 18 May (200 pairs on May) but few on 23rd (PWS). 200 pairs Ashfield probably reared 120Y (WRB). 300 (63 nests) Barbush 3 May but all failed and birds left by 15 May (MVB).

COMMON GULL *Larus canus (B,W)*
F Several hundred winter around Grangemouth suburbs (WRB).
C 130 Cambus 10 May were all immature (CJH).
S Birds feeding in Stirling garden Aug & Dec (RJ).
SWP Argaty: 100 on 10 Mar, 100 pairs on 10 May and still 60 on 23rd (PWS). 36 (9 nests) Barbush 3 May, survived better than BHG (MVB). 2 nests Monachlye Glen 8 Jun & 3 pairs Kirkton 4 May (DJP). 15 L.Oss 9 May (SS).

LESSER BLACK-BACKED GULL *Larus fuscus (b,S)*
F 1 wintered Grangemouth Jan & Dec (WRB). lst of spring: 4 Kinneil 7 & 13 Feb (GO DT). 20 pairs Zeneca site, at least 2 broods of 3Y (WRB).
C 20 on warehouse roofs Cambus 18 Aug, possibly nested (CJH).
S Last of autumn 8 L.Coulter 13 Nov (WRB).
SWP 2 Dunblane 7 Mar (BH). 2 pairs Argaty 20 Apr, only 1 on 24 Jun (PWS).

HERRING GULL *Larus argentatus (b?,S,W)*
F 3000 (90% immature) Kinneil tip 8 May (HEMD).
C 1100 Cambus 26 May & 1900 Tullibody Inch 23 Jul were mainly immatures (CJH).
S 2400 Fallin tip 14 Apr & 1800 on 27 Nov (CJH).

*ICELAND GULL *Larus glaucoides*
C 1 lst winter Cambus 29 Mar (CJH).

KITTIWAKE *Rissa tridactyla (P,w)*
F 103 -> E Skinflats 9 Sep (GO). 3 Blackness 17 Oct (CJH).
S 1 imm, newly killed by predator, Carron Bridge 12 Feb (AFw).

SANDWICH TERN *Sterna sandvicensis (P)*
F 2 Skinflats 7 May & up to 4 until 3 Jul (AB GO). 80 Kinneil 29 Aug (DMB) & 440 Blackness 29 Aug (CJH). 30 Bo'ness 1 Sep (AMcI). 100 Skinflats 12 Sep & 25 on 18th (DMB MVB).
C 8 Cambus 9 Aug, 3 on 15th, 40 on 28th (WB CJH SH).

COMMON TERN *Sterna hirundo (B)*
F 2 Skinflats 7 May & 35 R.Carron on 8th (GO), 12 Kinneil 9 May (CJH). At four nesting sites Grangemouth there were 56 birds on 16 May

with 56 nests on 23rd rising to 113 on 19 June, 139 nests overall with at least 60 and possibly 100 Y reared; most adults left between 25 July (when many flying Y) & 7 Aug though 11 broods and 1 sitting bird still there on last date (DMB). Last, 2 Kincardine Br 18 Sep (MVB).

C   1 ->W Cambus 14 Jun (CJH).

*GUILLEMOT *Uria aalge (W)*
F   6 Blackness 6 Mar (CJH).

*RAZORBILL *Alca tarda (w)*
F   4 Blackness 6 Mar (CJH).

ROCK DOVE / FERAL PIGEON *Columba livia (B,W)*
S   350 on tilled ground Cambuskenneth 28 Oct (CJH).
SWP   50 Dunblane through year (BH).

STOCK DOVE *Columba oenas (B,W)*
F   2 Skinflats16 Apr & 25 May, 3 on 8th (HEMD GO RS).
C   2 Myreton 8 May, 20 S.Alloa bridge 23 Jul (CJH).
S   6 Cambuskenneth 28 Oct (CJH).
SWP   4 Thornhill 20 Dec (CJH).

WOODPIGEON *Columba palumba (B,W)*
F   1000 Larbert 26 Feb (AMcI). 330 roosting in birch scrub Kinneil 26 Nov (GO). 150 in stubble Camelon 28 Nov (AS).
C   330 Menstrie 25 Dec (BRT). Scarce Tillicoultry-Dollar Nov-Dec, 10 per 10 km transect (CJH).

COLLARED DOVE *Streptopelia decaocto (B,W)*
F   stragglers Kinneil 23 Apr (flying W) & Skinflats 11 Nov (GO).
C   21 Menstrie 11 Dec, much as 1991 & 1992 (BRT).
SWP   2 Dunblane Jan-Apr & Dec (BH).

CUCKOO *Cuculus canorus (B)*
S   1 Cocksburn Res 2 May (CJH).
SWP   lst Menteith Hills 23 Apr & Leny on 30th (WRB DT). 1 Monachyle Glen 5 May, at 400m Glen Crotha on 11th (DJP).

*BARN OWL *Tyto alba (b,w)*
F   1 hunting by road Stenhousemuir, night of 21 Nov (AB).
SWP   1 Dunblane 30 Jan (SS).

TAWNY OWL *Strix aluco (B,W)*
F   1 Skinflats 20 Sep (GO RS).
C   Heard Menstrie 5&6 Feb (BRT).
SWP   Fewer in nest boxes at Trossachs & clutches small (HR).

LONG-EARED OWL *Asio otus (b,w)*
F   1 Skinflats 20 Sep (AB GO RS).
C   Pair bred Cambus, seen 25 Apr to August, 4 Fledged juvs 3 May with adult carrying voles to them (WB WRB CJH SH).
SWP   1 Deanston 6 Aug (SS).

SHORT-EARED OWL *Asio flammeus (b,W)*
F   Skinflats: 1 on 18 Jan, 2 on 7 Feb & 3 on 17th, 1 until 1 Apr; 1 on 5 Jun
      & 17 Jul; 1 on 29 Aug, 26 Sep & 11 Nov (AB DMB GO RS). Kinneil:1
      on 3rd, 2 on 4th & 1 on 19 Jan, 3 on 7 Feb & 5 on 15th, 4 on 7 Mar; 1
      on 15 Sep & 31 Dec (AB GO RS DT). 1 Limerigg 20 Oct (AMcI).
C   1 Cambus 9 & 30 Jan, 14 Apr. 1 Blackdevonmouth 21 Mar (CJH).
S   2 seen in Carron Valley in summer (AFw).
SWP   1 Thornhill 26 Jan (SS). 1 Lecropt 9 Feb (CJH).

*NIGHTJAR *Caprimulgus europaeus*
SWP   1 singing in south section of Queen Elizabeth Forest Park in June (per
      Forest Enterprise).

SWIFT *Apus apus (B)*
F   1 over M9 Falkirk 9 May (CJH). 1 Skinflats 28 Apr (RS), 100 on 22 Jul
      (GO). 25 Jupiter WG in cold weather in Jun (WRB). 2 Larbert 23 Aug
      (DT).
S   lst BoA 26 Apr, main arrival 11 May; 50 on 2 Aug, 70 on 5th, 30 on 13th,
      last 10 on 16th (DMB CJH). 3 Stirling 11 May (RJ), few after 17 Aug,
      last 1 on 21 Aug (DT). 1 Airthrey 25 Aug (MVB).
SWP   2 Ashfield 12 May, 5 AoT (WRB). 12 Blairdrummond 16 May (PWS). 3
      Dunblane 19 May, 20 on 20-30 Jul, last 3 on 15 Aug (BH).

*KINGFISHER *Alcedo atthis (b,w)*
F   1 Carronshore 30 Oct (AB). 2 on R.Avon at Grangemouth early Dec
      (per WRB).
C   1 pair reared broods of 5 & 4 (MC). 1 Cambus 14 Aug (SH).
SWP   1 Ashfield 13 Nov (WRB).

GREEN WOODPECKER *Picus viridis (B,W)*
F   4 (prob juv) Roughcastle 18 Aug (AS).
C   Heard Menstrie from Apr, also 1 on 25 & 28 Dec (BRT). 1 Harvieston
      2 Feb (CJH).
S   2 Plean CP 28 Mar (DT).
SWP   At 2 sites L.Ard Forest Jun-Jul (CJH), calling on 22 Aug (RAB). At
      Balquhidder in Apr & Oct (DJP). 1 Callander 2 Apr (PWS).1 Menteith
      Hills 6 Apr, Lake of Menteith on 18 Apr & 3 Aug (RAB DT).

GREAT SPOTTED WOODPECKER *Dendrocopus major (B,W)*
F   AoTs at Dunmore 21 Apr & Maddiston on 28th (AMcI). Probably 2
      AoT Howierig mid-Jul (AS). 1 Jupiter WG 2 Nov (WRB).
C   1 Harviestoun 10 Nov (CJH).
S   1 Blairlogie 3 Apr (CJH). 2 Mine Wood 22 May & 1 on 26 Dec (DMB).
SWP   1 Dunblane 8 Feb (BH). 1 Ardeonaig 2 Apr (PWS). 1 L.Ard Forest 18 &
      23 May (CJH). 2 with brood Doune 6 June (DMB).
      (This must be a highly underrecorded species, Ed)

SKYLARK *Alauda arvensis (B,W)*
F   70 Skinflats 2 Nov & 50 on 7th (AB AMcI). 180 Kinneil 31 Dec (MVB).

C   60 Gogar 29 Oct & 27 Nov (CJH), 80 ->W 28 Dec & 200 there (Stubble) on 30th (BRT).
S   Song Kippenmuir 6 Feb (DT). 15 Cambuskenneth 10 Feb, 20 in tight & wary flock Kippenrait 11 Apr (CJH).
SWP   Song Thornhill 5 Feb (SS). 4 ->NW Blairdrummond 7 Feb; 102 Gargunnock 11 Nov, 35 Drip Moss on 22nd, 100+85+73 Thornhill 20 Dec (CJH). 4-5 AoT Ashfield Feb-Jun, 5 AoT Bows-Cromlix 17 Apr (WRB). Little change on Blairdrummond spring transect (CJH).

SAND MARTIN *Riparia riparia (B)*
F   1 Carronshore 21 Mar (AB).
C   1st Gartmorn Dam 23 Mar (MC).
S   7 Airthrey 7 Apr & 20 on 8th (DMB).
SWP   3 Lake of Menteith 14 Mar & 30 on 31st (DT). 10 Blairdrummond 23 Mar (PWS). 1st Dunblane 1 Apr & 5 on 3rd, some nest holes appeared on earthslip but abandoned after fenced along top (BH). 200 Barbush 24 Apr (WRB).

SWALLOW *Hirundo rustica (B)*
F   1 Skinflats16 Apr (GO). Some ->W Kinneil 6 Sept (DT).
C   1st Gartmorn 3 Apr (MC), Menstrie 21 Apr (BRT). 20 hawking Cambus Pool in bad weather on 15 May (CJH). 500 at roost Tullibody Inch 4 Sept, harried by Sparrowhawk (DMB).
S   3 Craigforth 11 Apr (DMB), 3 Airthrey on 16th (MVB).
SWP   4 Dunblane 11 Apr & 20 juv on 1 & 2 Oct (BH). 1 Lake of Menteith 11 Apr, 2 Ashfield on 18th (WRB). 1 Thornhill 21 Apr, Menteith Hills on 23rd (AMcI DT). 5 Aberfoyle 22 Sept (DT).
SWP   1st Kinlochard & Aberfoyle 2 Apr (R.Duel LTB). Last Balquhidder 17 Sep (DJP).

HOUSE MARTIN *Delichon urbica (B)*
F   1 Slamannan 11 Nov (TDS) - *exceptionally late date*, Ed.
C   1st Menstrie 2 May, nestbuilding from 11th, 20 birds on 18th; 65 on 10 Sep, last 2 on 23rd (BRT).
S   1 Airthrey 8 Apr (DMB), Stirling 24 Apr (RJ). Last BoA 4 on 12 Oct (CJH).
SWP   1st Thornhill 21 Apr (AMcI), Menteith Hills 23 Apr (DT). 1st Ashfield 25 Apr, 8 pairs, last 3 on 8 Oct (WRB). 1st Dunblane 27 May (8 on 29th), 2 on 2 Oct (BH).

TREE PIPIT *Anthus trivialis (B)*
C   4 AoT Wood Hill, 3 AoT Dollar Glen (MC).
SWP   2 sg Thornhill 10 Apr (SS), Menteith Hills on 23rd (DT), Kilmahog on 30th (WRB). In breeding season at Aberfoyle, L.Ard Forest (HEMD CJH). Heard Ashfield 12 Aug & ->S Dunblane on 29th (WRB MVB).

MEADOW PIPIT *Anthus pratensis (B,W)*
F   A few wintered Jupiter WG Feb-Apr and from Sep (WRB).
C   5 by floodwater Dollar 24 Dec (CJH).

S   25 Arnprior 24 Oct (DT).
SWP   Some Balquhidder 6 Apr & abundant by 13th (DJP). 38 Thornhill 20
         Dec (CJH).

*ROCK PIPIT *Anthus petrosus (w)*
F   1 Blackness 17 Oct (CJH).
C   1 Forthbank, Cambus, 26 Dec (BRT).

*YELLOW WAGTAIL *Motacilla flava*
F   1 Skinflats 18 Apr (WRB).

GREY WAGTAIL *Motacilla cinerea (B,w)*
F   1 Falkirk (Westquarter) 18 Apr (AMcI). Through year at Jupiter WG,
         pair Apr-May but did not breed (WRB). 1 Kinneil 26 Nov (GO).
C   Menstrie in Apr (BRT). 1 by R.Devon at Dollar 10 Nov & 24 Dec (CJH).
S   1 in Stirling centre 26 Jan & 22 Oct (DT). 2 AoT R.Allan (Kippenrait) 8
         Mar, 14 Apr (CJH PWS). Ad with newly fledged Juv BoA 20 May
         (DMB) (*1.5 km from known AoT*, Ed).
SWP   2 AoT Dunblane in Apr, juv on 27 May (BH). Only a fair breeding
         success (HR).

PIED WAGTAIL *Motacilla alba (B,W)*
F   Birds of the *alba* subspecies seen at Skinflats: 1 on 25 Mar, 5 on 16 Apr,
         4 on 20th, 2 on 22nd & 23rd (AB GO); also 1 gathering insects at
         Powbridge on 18 Jun (AB) (*? suggests breeding*, Ed).
C   Juvs seen Menstrie 28 May (BRT). A few Dollar Nov-Dec (CJH).
SWP   2 through year Dunblane (BH). Breeding numbers seemed low (HR).
         No change on Blairdrummond spring transect; only 1 in 10 Km
         Thornhill 20 Dec (CJH).

DIPPER *Cinclus cinclus (B,W)*
F   1 Falkirk 18 Apr (AMcI). 1 Bonnywater Oct-Dec (AS).
C   Menstrie Burn Apr & Dec (BRT).
S   2 AoT R.Allan (Kippenrait) 14 Apr (CJH). 2 on Pow Burn S of Kippen
         19 Dec (RJ).
SWP   3 through year Dunblane, displaying 21 Feb (BH). Only fair breeding
         succes (HR).

WREN *Troglodytes troglodytes (B,W)*
C   Fledged Y seen Menstrie 28 May (BRT).
SWP   No change on Blairdrummond spring transect (CJH).

HEDGE SPARROW *Accentor modularis (B,W)*
SWP   Only 1/4 as frequent as Robin on Blairdrummond spring transect but
         no change (CJH).

ROBIN *Erithacus rubecula (B,W)*
S   Autumn song Airthrey 13 Aug (CJH).
SWP   4 together in Dunblane garden Feb (BH). 17 records per 8km spring
         transect Blairdrummond, increase of 50% from 1992 (CJH).

REDSTART *Phoenicurus phoenicurus (B)*
S   Imm in Stirling garden 19 & 21 Aug (RJ).
C   Pair bred Wood Hill (MC).
SWP   1 Ashfield 12 Apr, 2 M Kilmahog on 30th (WRB). Pair at nestbox Ardeonaig 29 Apr (PWS). 40 nests at Trossachs colony reared 215 Y (HR).

WHINCHAT *Saxicola torquata (B)*
F   M Skinflats 6 May, F+4Y on 23 Jul (GO), 1 on 22 Aug (AB). Pair feeding Y Howierigg 19 Jul (ASt). 1 Grangemouth 29 Aug (DMB). 2 Kinneil 3 Sep (DT).
S   lst Cocksburn Res 2 May - M with song ending with Chaffinch flourish (CJH).
SWP   lst Callander 30 Apr (WRB). 2 AoT L.Ard Forest in 120 Ha replanted conifer (CJH). 1 Argaty 18 May, 2 Stronachlachar on 28th (PWS). None seen in breeding season (DT).

*STONECHAT *Saxicola torquata (b,w)*
F   2F Kinneil 28 Nov (DT). 2 L.Ellrig 28 Sep (RS).
C   F Blackdevonmouth 21 Mar; F Dollar 24 Dec (CJH).
S   F Cambuskenneth 25 Jan (CJH). Pair Carron Valley 11 Sep (DO).
SWP   M Flanders Moss 13 Mar (SS). 1 L.Doine 14 Apr (DJP). 1 Stronachlachar 28 May (PWS).

WHEATEAR *Oenanthe oenanthe (B)*
F   3 Skinflats 18 Apr & 1 on 20th (AB GO). 2 Kinneil 1 & 12 Apr, 1 on 14th, 5 on 6 May (CJH GO RS DT). 2 Skinflats 22 Aug (AB), 2 Kinneil 3 Sep (GO). 1 Jupiter WG (Greenland race) 14 Aug (WRB). Last Fannyside 5 Oct (AMcI).
S   M Cringate & Cairnoch Lodge 11 Apr, 1 Thornhill on 13th (SS DT). F Cambus 8 May (SH).
SWP   1 L.Doine 14 Apr (DJP). 3 Cromlix 17 Apr (WRB). Last 1 L.Arklet 4 Sep (AMcI).

*RING OUSEL *Turdus torquatus (b)*
SWP   F Balquhidder 11 Apr (AMcI).

BLACKBIRD *Turdus merula (B,W)*
S   3 taking Cotoneaster berries BoA 6-11 Jan (CJH).
SWP   10 juv together Dunblane 18 Aug, 15 on 13 Dec (BH). Decrease of 27% on Blairdrummond spring transect (CJH).

FIELDFARE *Turdus pilaris (W)*
F   150 L.Ellrig 8 Jan (CJH). Many Skinflats10th Oct (AB). 150 Fannyside 20 Oct & Garbethill on 14 Nov, 60 Airth 2 Nov (AMcI). 45 Bonnybridge 8 Nov (AS).
C   250 Kennetpans 9 Jan & 450 on 24th, 75 Forestmill 14 Feb. 20 Gartmorn on 20 Oct (CJH DT). 40 Gogar 30 Dec (BRT).
S   150 Cambuskenneth 25 Jan, 60 Arnprior 6 Feb & 100 Cringate 11 Apr. 5 BoA 11 Oct, 300 Gargunnock, 200 Kippenmuir & 700 Arnprior 24

Oct, 232 Gargunnock 11 Nov (MVB CJH DT).

SWP   100 Braes of Doune 2 Feb, 60 Lecropt 4 Mar (CJH). 30 Ashfield 15 Mar & 200 ->SW on 14 Nov (WRB). 150 Thornhill 12 Apr (SS). 5 ->SW Dunblane 9 Oct (MVB). 500 Blairdrummond Moss & 150 Torrie on 24 Oct (DT).

SONG THRUSH *Turdus philomenos (B,W)*

F   Many Skinflats 10 Oct (AB).

C   2 Cambus 27 Nov were presumably responsible for the hundreds of smashed shells of *Cepaea nemoralis* (CJH).

SWP   No change on Blairdrummond spring transect, now as frequent as Blackbird (CJH). A few Dunblane through year but 5 on 3 Mar (BH). 2 AoT Ashfield (WRB).

REDWING *Turdus iliacus (W)*

F   50 S.Alloa 8 Jan (PWS). 6 Skinflats 6 Oct & many on 10th (AB GO). 6 Garbethill 6 Oct, 200 on 20th & 40 on 14 Nov (AMcI).

C   15 Wood Hill 27 Dec foraged in leaf litter with Blackbirds; 40 Gogar on 30th with Fieldfares and Starlings; 4 Menstrie stripped a Holly of berries 26-29 Dec (BRT).

S   Up to 20 BoA stripped a Cotoneaster of berries 6-14 Jan (this bush previously misidentifed as Stranvesia). 62 Cocksburn Res 10 Oct (CJH), 350 Arnprior on 24th (DT). 50 inside Mine Wood 26 Dec foraged in leaf litter (snow on fields) (DMB).

SWP   300 Braes of Doune 25 Jan (PWS). lst autumn Ashfield 2 on 4 Oct (WRB). 18 Dunblane7 Oct (BH). 500 Blairdrummond Moss 24 Oct (DT).

MISTLE THRUSH *Turdus viscivorus (B,W)*

S   12 Cambusbarron 1 Aug (RJ).

*GRASSHOPPER WARBLER *Locustella naevia (B)*

F   Song Skinflats & Carronshore 25 Apr (AB), 3 Skinflats 5 May and one until 18 Jul (GO RS).

C   Song Cambus 24 Apr & 27 Jul (WB).

SWP   Song Blairdrummond carse 29 Apr to 20 May (CJH).

SEDGE WARBLER *Acrocephalus schoenobaenus (B)*

F   2 Falkirk 24 Apr (AMcI). 2 Skinflats 1 May (RS), 4 on 4 Sep (DT).

C   lst Cambus 27 Apr (WB), 1 AoT through May, last 14 Aug (CJH SH AMcI). lst Gartmorn Dam 22 Apr, 4 AoT (MC).

SWP   lst Thornhill 4 May (SS). 1AoT Ashfield (WRB). Only 1 on Blairdrummond transect in May (CJH).

*LESSER WHITETHROAT *Sylvia curruca*

F   1 singing by Polmont Res 6 May (WRB).

WHITETHROAT *Sylvia communis (B)*

F   lst (2) Camelon 24 Apr (AMcI); 2 Skinflats 26 Apr & 5 on 7 May, last there on 12 Sep; 1 Carronshore 28 Apr (AB GO RS). 1 AoT Jupiter WG

(WRB). 3 Kinneil 13 Jun (DT). Pair feeding Y Howierig 19 Jul (ASt).
C   3 pairs bred Gartmorn & 4 pairs along Devon Way (MC). 2 AoT
     Cambus 15 May (CJH).
SWP 2 Dunblane 12 May, 1 AoT Argaty (PWS). 1 AoT Blairdrummond
     transect (none in 1992) (CJH).

GARDEN WARBLER *Sylvia borin (B)*
SWP lst Aberfoyle 4 May (HEMD), Ashfield (2 AoT) 9 May (WRB). 1 AoT
     Blairdrummond transect (CJH).

BLACKCAP *Sylvia atricapilla (B)*
F   1 Polmont Res 6 May (WRB). M Skinflats 7 May & 13 Jun, last 12 Sep
     (AB GO).
C   Pair Cambus 30 Apr (WRB). M Menstrie 3 May (BRT). lst Gartmorn
     Dam 16 Apr, 6 pairs bred (MC). F wintered Dollar 30 Dec to Mar 94
     (SH).
S   M&F wintered 92-93 in Stirling garden (JB). M in Stirling garden 27
     Oct, F on 15 & 31 Dec (at Snowberry, RJ).

WOOD WARBLER *Phylloscopus sibilitrax (B)*
F   Pair + 3 Y Howierig 19 Jul (ASt). *Few breeding records for district* (Ed).
C   lst (2) Aberfoyle 4 May (HEMD). 4 AoT Dollar 29 May, single pairs
     Woodhill & Gartmorn (Cow park) (WB MC).
SWP lst Kilmahog 30 Apr (WRB). Sg L.Ard Forest 19 May (CJH). 4 M
     L.Achray (Ben AÕan path) 14 Jun (HEMD). Record number of nests
     found at Trossachs site and high breeding success (HR).

CHIFFCHAFF *Phylloscopus collybita (B)*
F   4 sg Howierig 19 Jul (ASt). 1Falkirk 28 May (AMcI).
C   lst Gartmorn 2 Apr (MC), 6 Apr (WB). 1 AoT Menstrie from 7 May
     (BRT).
S   Song Airthrey 2 Apr (MVB) & Blairlogie on 3rd (CJH), BoA on 11th
     (PWS). 1 Cambuskenneth 18 Apr (KA). 2 Plean CP 10 Apr (DT).
SWP Wintering bird at L.Chon in mid Feb (R.Duel). lst Lake of Menteith 31
     Mar (DT). Singing Dunblane in June (WRB MVB).

WILLOW WARBLER *Phylloscopus trochilus (B)*
F   1 Kinneil 14 Apr, widespread by 18th (DT). lst Skinflats 16 Apr, last on
     12 Sep (AB GO). lst Falkirk 20 Apr, many on 26th (AMcI). 3 AoT
     Jupiter WG (WRB). 19 broods Howierig 19 Jul (ASt).
C   3 sg Cambus 25 Apr (SH).
S   lst imm of autumn in Stirling garden 7 Aug (RJ).
SWP lst Ashfield 10 Apr (WRB), Lake of Menteith 21st (AMcI), Dunblane
     25th (BH), Monachyle Glen 28th (DJP). In spruce ptn at 300m Braes of
     Doune (WRB). 6 AoT Blairdrummond transect 29 Apr & 3 May, only
     1 on 19th & 20th after severe weather (CJH). Last Dunblanc 19 Sep
     (MVB).

GOLDCREST *Regulus regulus (B,W)*
F   Through year at Skinflats & bred in pine copse (AB). 2 wintered Jupiter WG from 2 Nov (WRB).
C   1 in scrub below Menstrie Crag 1 Jan & 1 in garden in severe weather on 12th (BRT).
SWP   2 AoT on Blairdrummond transect, no change (CJH).

SPOTTED FLYCATCHER *Muscicapa striata (B)*
F   2 AoT Howierig 19 Jul (ASt). 1 Skinflats 16 & 25 Aug, 12 Sep (AB).
SWP   2 Kinbuck 19 May (PWS). 1AoT Ashfield (WRB). 2 L.Ard Forest 12 Aug (CJH).

PIED FLYCATCHER *Ficedula hypoleuca (b)*
SWP   2M Kilmahog 30 Apr & Aberfoyle 4 May (WRB HEMD). 58 nest attempts fledged 291 Y at Trossachs nestbox colony (HR).

LONG-TAILED TIT *Aegithalos caudatus (B,W)*
F   11 BoŌness 22 Feb (RS). 15 Jupiter WG 23 Nov (WRB). 10 Bonnybridge (Seabegs) 8 Dec (AS).
C   6 Menstrie 3 Jan (BRT). 9 Gartmorn 23 Oct (CJH).
S   8 BoA 13 Jan & 6 on 8 Mar (PWS).
SWP   12 Dunblane 24 Jan, 3 at feeder in Jan (BH). 10 Kirkton Glen 26 Oct (DJP).

COAL TIT *Parus ater (B,W)*
SWP   Commoner than Blue Tit in mixed woodland Blairdrummond through May (CJH).

BLUE TIT *Parus caeruleus (B,W)*
C   12 with Great Tits in scrub Menstrie Crag 1 Jan (BRT).
SWP   3 AoT Blairdrummond transect in May (CJH). More at Trossachs nestbox project & good breeding success (HR).

GREAT TIT *Parus major (B,W)*
SWP   3 AoT Blairdrummond transect in May (CJH). Good breeding success at Trossachs nestbox project (HR).

TREECREEPER *Certhia familiaris (B,W)*
S   2 climbing on stone wall at BoA for 2 min on 30 Apr, adult fed juv (CJH).

*GREAT GREY SHRIKE *Lanius excubitor*
S   1 Carron Valley Forest (W) 6 & 7 Nov (JWy).

JAY *Garrulus glandarius (B,W)*
F   2 or 3 family parties with at least 12 birds at Howierig 19 Jul (ASt), 1 there on 22 Nov (AS). 1 Bonnybridge (Seabegs) Oct-Dec (AS).
C   Single pairs in summer Gartmornhill, Birkhill, Wood Hill, Cowpark (MC). Seems to be increasing Clacks but only 1 Tillicoultry-Dollar 10 Nov in 17 km transect (CJH).

S   1 Torwood 28 Nov (AB).
        No significant reports from main area in SWP.

MAGPIE Pica pica (B,W)
C   5 Cambus 26 Dec (BRT).
S   13 Cambuskenneth 28 Oct (CJH).
SWP   10 Lecropt (prob roost) 9 Feb; 1 Blairdrummond 7 Feb but none seen
        on spring transects nearby. 1 Thornhill (9.5km transect) 20 Dec (CJH).
        1 Ashfield Mar-Apr, disappeared (WRB). 2 Dunblane (Newton Cres)
        by summer - lst seen here (MVB).

JACKDAW *Corvus monedula (B,W)*
C   200 Tillicoultry 6 Feb (CJH).

ROOK *Corvus frugilegus (B,W)*
        Rookery counts: BoA(N), 69; BoA(S) 141; Witches Crag 48; Myretoun
        81. Total 339. Young out of nest at Menstrie on 28 May (BRT).

CARRION CROW *Corvus corone (B,W)*
F   100 Kinneil 9 May (CJH), 1 'Hoodie' there on 23 Apr (GO).
SWP   21 Sheriffmuir 24 Apr (MVB).
S   1 with Mole Airthrey 19 Aug (MVB).

RAVEN *Corvus corax (B,W)*
SWP   13 ranges checked, 12 pairs; 6 successful pairs raised 18Y & 3 more an
        unknown number, one half grown Y killed by mammalian predator
        (PS-A).
        More low ground records than usual : 4 Lundie (Braes of Doune) 19
        Jan (PWS); pair Thornhill 23 & 30 Jan, 1 on 3 Feb (SS); 1 Lake of
        Menteith 14 Mar (DT); 4 Cromlix 17 Apr (WRB); 2 L.Ard Forest 24 June
        (CJH); 2 over Dunblane 4 Sep (MVB). 2 Airthrey 28 Jan (DMB).

STARLING *Sturnus vulgaris (B,W)*
S   lst juv seen BoA 24 May (CJH).
SWP   No large flocks on Thornhill carse transects Nov-Dec, max 105 on 20
        Dec (CJH).

HOUSE SPARROW *Passer domesticus (B,W)*
C   Records on transects in Devon Valley Nov-Dec west of Dollar
        restricted to the town and its outskirts, max flock only 6 on 22 Dec
        (CJH).

TREE SPARROW *Passer montanus (B,W)*
F   40 Skinflats 21 Nov & 4 Dec (AB).
C   4 Cambus 14 Jun, juv food begging (lst breeding in this locality, CJH).
        4 Gartmorn 10 Apr & 16 on 4 Oct (WB). 84 Kennetpans 7 Feb (MVB),
        5 on 24 Oct (DMB).
SWP   Pair nested successfully in Trossachs (HR) (*unusual area & habitat,* Ed).
        30 Lecropt 12 Dec (DT). Widespread on Carse of Stirling, max 40 Frew
        13 November, 65 Drip Moss (Baad) 30 Jan (MVB) & 10 on 22 Nov
        (CJH).

CHAFFINCH *Fringilla coelebs (B,W)*
F   200 Larbert 13 Mar (AMcI).
C   80 Menstrie 11 Dec & 400 in stubble at Gogar on 30 Dec (BRT).
S   500 Arnprior 6 Feb (DT).
SWP   Commonest breeding passerine in mixed wood transect Blairdrummond, 14 records per km, up 60% over 1992 (CJH). lst song Thornhill 7 Feb (SS). 200 Ashfield 31 Oct (WRB).

BRAMBLING *Fringilla montifringilla (W)*
F   1 Skinflats 7 Feb, 13 Kinneil 26 Nov (GO) & 6 on 31 Dec (MVB). 20 Carronshore 27 & 28 Dec (AB). 30 Garbethill 10 Nov, 110 Slamannan 10 Nov (DO) & 23 on 31 Dec (AMcI). 50 Threaprig 1 Dec (JS).
C   70 on stubble with Chaffinches Menstrie 30 Dec (BRT).
S   4 (3M) Arnprior 6 Feb, 7 on 24 Oct (DT). 1 Airthrey 23 Nov (DMB).
SWP   10 Killin 17 Apr (PWS). 2 Ashfield 31 Oct to end Nov (WRB). 3 Thornhill 20 Nov (SS).

GREENFINCH *Carduelis chloris (B,W)*
F   100 Kinneil 12 & 31 Dec (DMB MVB).
C   150 Menstrie 25 Dec, also fed on nuts (BRT).
SWP   40 Ashfield 31 Oct (WRB).

GOLDFINCH *Carduelis carduelis (B,W)*
F   26 Jupiter WG 5 Mar (WRB). 20 Kincardine Bridge 31 Dec (MVB). Through year at Skinflats (AB).
C   5 Devonmouth 1 Apr & 5 Dollar 24 Dec (CJH). Pair Menstrie Burn 28 May. 16 Alva 27 Dec (BRT).
S   18 Airthrey 28 Jan (MVB). 12 Myothill 13 Oct & 9 Gargunnock 11 Nov (CJH).
SWP   18 Ashfield 4 Oct (WRB).

SISKIN *Carduelis spinus (B,W)*
F   6 Skinflats 31 Mar & 1 to 28 Apr (GO). 1 family party Howierig 19 Jul (ASt) - Appears to be first breeding record for District, Ed.. 60 Bonnybridge (Seabegs) 1 Dec (AS).
C   18 Gartmorn 7 Feb (WB). 2 on peanuts within half hour of lst provision of winter at Menstrie 27 Dec (BRT).
S   15 L.Laggan 24 Oct (DT). Song BoA 11 May & 17 Jul but no signs of breeding. 20 on seeding grass Carron Valley Res 28 Jul (CJH). Max 4 on peanuts Stirling from 5 Nov (RJ).
SWP   70 Callander 21 Mar (JT). Many L.Venachar 18 Oct (CJH), 25 Brig o'Turk 28 Nov (WRB). 50 Firbush Point (L.Tay) 20 November (C&AS).

LINNET *Carduelis cannabina (B,W)*
F   400 Kinneil 31 Dec (MVB). 13 Airth shore 13 Apr (CJH), 12 Falkirk 24 Apr (AMcI).
C   27 (in song) Longcarse 19 Feb , 120 in rape stubble Gogar 19 Oct (CJH). 150 Kennetpans 24 Oct & 300 on 28 Nov (DMB MVB).
SWP   150 Frew 30 Jan (MVB). 30 Thornhill 20 Dec (CJH).

TWITE *Carduelis flavirostris (b,.W)*
F   15 Dunmore 24 Jan (DMB). 50 S.Alloa 30 Jan attacked by Sparrowhawk. 65 Airth shore 28 Nov feeding on Sea Aster (CJH). 15 Skinflats 7 Nov & 45 on 20 Dec (AB DF). 20 Kinneil 26 Nov (GO).
SWP   2 pairs Callander (Glen Artney) 10 Jul (DMB). 2 Kinbuck 19 May (PWS) - *late date for low ground,* Ed.

REDPOLL *Carduelis flammea (B,W)*
F   1 Jupiter WG 28 Jan (WRB). 2 Skinflats 28 Apr (GO). 1 Falkirk 24 Apr (AMcI). 1 or 2 AoT Howierig 19 Jul (ASt).
SWP   1 Dunblane 27 May (BH), 1 L.Voil 11 Jul (DJP). 35 in birches Milour Moor & 40 Cromlix on 17 Apr; Pair bred Ashfield (WRB).
         (*Seems local as breeding species but probably often overlooked,* Ed)

BULLFINCH *Pyrrhula pyrrhula (B,W)*
F   6 broods Howierig 19 Jul (ASt).
S   5 Carron Valley Res 27 Dec (CJH).
SWP   12 Ben An 23 Feb (WRB). 2 Monachyle Glen 14 Mar (DJP).

COMMON CROSSBILL *Loxia curvirostra (b,W)*
S   50 Carron Valley Forest 3 Aug (JM), singing there on 28 Jul, a few on 11, 19 & 27 Dec (AB WRB CJH). 10 -> SW Airthrey 23 Nov (DMB).
SWP   7 L.Ard Forest 19 Jun (CJH). 2 Menteith Hills 23 Apr, 1 L.Rusky 5 Oct & 7 on 5 Dec (DT), 2 Stronachlachar 17 Oct (MT).

*SNOW BUNTING *Plectrophenax nivalis (W)*
S   1 Cambuskenneth 25 Jan (CJH). *No doubt still frequent on the winter hills* (Ed).

YELLOWHAMMER *Emberiza citrinella (B,W)*
F   26 Skinflats 12 Feb (RS). 20 Dunmore 25 Feb (PWS), 58 Airth shore 2 Apr & 40 on 28 Nov (CJH). 2 AoT Maddiston 26 Apr (AMcI).
C   30 Kennetpans 24 Jan (MVB).
S   15 Cambuskenneth 25 Jan (CJH).
SWP   1 AoT Ashfield, 15 on 31 Oct (WRB). 30 Blairdrummond Moss 9 Jan (DT). 50 Frew 20 Mar; 40 Lecropt 18 Dec (MVB).

REED BUNTING *Emberiza schoeniclus (B,W)*
F   2 broods Howierig 19 Jul (ASt).
C   1 Cambus 21 Mar & 2 AoT 22 Jul, 4 birds on 14 Aug. 8 Kennetpans 26 Dec (CJH SH).
SWP   4 Thornhill 20 Dec (CJH).

*CORN BUNTING *Miliaria calandra (b,w)*
F   1 Letham (by M876) 22 Apr (WRB). M in song Skinflats on 30 Jun (GO).
S   M in song Powbridge 13 Jun (DT) (*2 km from Letham record,* Ed).

Additions to 1992 Report

HONEY BUZZARD *Pernis apivorus*
F   On 7 July 1992 at Skinflats an adult soared in from the R.Forth and continued on to the SW. Full description supplied, the salient points included : size as common Buzzard but head small and protruding on a thin neck, wings seemed narrower and held flat. Underwing whitish with dark tips to primaries and secondaries giving a dark trailing edge, also double dark bar on underwing coverts. Chin whitish, breast dark and rest of underparts whitish with dark barring. Undertail whitish with two dark bars plus a terminal bar (R.Shand).

HEN HARRIER *Circus cyaneus*
SWP   2 Upper Kelty Water 9 Jul & 1 Menteith Hills on 19th (JT).

HOUSE MARTIN *Delichon urbica*
SWP   30 nests at Arie waterhouse (Kelty Water) 9 Jul (JT).

STONECHAT *Saxicola torquata*
SWP   1 Bochastle (Callander) 4 Jul, 1 L.Doine on 5th, 1 Kelty Water on 7th (JT).

TWITE *Caduelis flavirostris*
SWP   4 Arie Dam (Kelty) 7 Jul (JT).

Correction to 1992 Report

BRENT GOOSE *(Branta bernicla)*
F   1 (light form) Skinflats 18 Oct (DMB). (*not 16, Ed mistake*)

BOOK NOTE

At the Watershed: a discussion paper on integrated catchment management for Scotland. Editor Alastair Stephen. Scottish Wildlife and Countryside Links (SWCL). 1994. 26pp. 0 9518582 2 X. £5.

SWCL's Freshwater Working Party in association with Farming & Wildlife Advisory Group; Fish Conservation Centre; RSPB; SCP; SWT; WWF and others recommends statutory bodies and non-government organisations (NGDs) join together in an initiative to tackle the urgent problems associated with managing fresh waters using the recognised framework of Integrated Catchment Management (ICM) – such as algal blooms (Loch Leven), Tay flooding and Loch Lomond problems, rivers and streams pollutions, mine waters....

L.C.

BOOK NOTES/REVIEWS (Naturalist)

THE NORTHERN EMERALD:
AN ADDITION TO THE FORTH VALLEY DRAGONFLY FAUNA

John T. Knowler and John Mitchell

On 23 July 1994, a dragonfly recording visit to a relict forest bog near Loch Ard, Aberfoyle, revealed the unexpected presence of the Northern Emerald (*Somatochlora arctica* Zett.).

Despite the Northern Emerald being an exceptionally fast and high flyer, a male was eventually caught for examination to confirm the identity. A female was also present, being seen basking in the sunlight on one of the lower branches of a tall conifer at the edge of the bog. Mating or egg-laying was not observed, but the habitat with its well developed 'hump and hollow' sphagnum cover interspersed with small pools would appear particularly suitable for breeding.

Although the Northern Emerald was first collected in Scotland in 1844 from the Rannoch area of Perthshire (Selys-Longchamps 1846), these sightings from the upper Forth Valley represent the first instance of the species being found in the south of the county. The Loch Ard site is also the most southerly locality known in Britain (excluding Ireland) for this rare boreo-alpine dragonfly.

REFERENCE

SELYS-LONGCHAMPS, E de. 1846. Revision of the British Libellulidae. *The Annals and Magazine of Natural History* 18, 217-227.

HERMITAGE WOOD: a woodland conservation project. Les Hudson. *Staneybreeks!* journal of the Stirling Civic Trust. vol 1 (2) Spring 1994, pp16-20.
This short paper describes the first stages of implementing the David Shaftoe Hermitage Wood Management Plan of 1992, clearing and restoring the network of paths, and tackling the dense growth of *Rhododendron Ponticum* in the ancient woodland section. The first half of the paper is about the history of the wood. It is all a valuable addition to the section on this University woodland in FN&H's 1986 *Airthrey and Bridge of Allan* – a guide. Much work will continue under the management plan, now with supervision by the University's Environmental Science Department.

THE 19th MAN AND LANDSCAPE SYMPOSIUM – Alloa, Nov. 1993. Notes on the papers presented are recorded in the *Clackmannanshire Field Studies Society Newsletter* no. 52 April 1994, pp14-22.

MOUNTAIN HARES IN THE OCHIL HILLS

Alex Tewnion

The Ochil Hills are a range of grassy, rounded heights stretching eastwards about 45 km from Sheriff Muir, near Dunblane, and measuring about 13 km from north to south at their broadest point between Strath Earn and the Devon Valley. The group is divided by two adjacent glens, the northwards running Glen Eagles and the northwest-southeast aligned section of Glen Devon to the south; and the highest hills, comprising all those over 610m in altitude, are situated in the western portion. The observations on the Scottish mountain hare *Lepus timidus scoticus* described in this article were made mainly in the western section, and especially in two areas which have extensive growths of heather *Calluna vulgaris*, the principal food of mountain hares (Flux 1970). One of these sites (Area A, see map) lies on the western side of the head of Glen Eagles, to the west and south of the little rocky peak called West Craigs. It measures approximately 77 ha. The other main site studied (Area B) includes the highest slopes and plateaus of Mickle Corum, Greenforet Hill and Blairdenon Hill and an extensive stretch of grassy and haggy ground lying east and north of Blairdenon Hill. The upper reaches of Area B have little heather but do have a good growth of blaeberry *Vaccinium myrtillus*, another food of mountain hares. A north-south running fence immediately to the east of the headwaters of the River Devon provides an artificial boundary between Area B and Alva Moss, another heather-covered haggy area stretching eastwards to the foot of Ben Buck. Area B is about 200 ha while the main part of Alva Moss (named C on map) which was also explored on occasion covers about 75 ha.

In addition to the main study areas, notes were also made on any mountain hares seen elsewhere on the Ochil Hills, concentrating on the period 1971 to date. These notes were made incidentally to a study of mountain hare behaviour and population which I carried out from 1968-82 in an area of Choinneachain Hill. This lies above Loch Turret Reservoir 7 km northwest of Crieff. Whenever the Glen Turret road became difficult or impassable because of snow or ice, I chose the Ochil Hills as an alternative from 1971 onwards.

Earlier reference to mountain hares on the Ochils are scarce. According to Ritchie (1920) the mountain hare is indigenous in the Ochils and the Campsies, but not farther south. Rintoul and Baxter (1935) mention that in 1891 "it was fairly numerous in the Ochils above Tillicoultry", while Proctor (in Timms 1974) states that C. J. Henty "has recently noted that on the Ochils this species is particularly common on the heather hags and that up to 40 have been seen at a time." Also, "There is a feeling that the Scottish Mountain Hare has decreased in numbers in recent years although evidence is lacking." Violent fluctuations in populations of this species are well known however, and R. Hewson (in Corbet and Harris 1991) states, "... maximum numbers in Scotland may be 2-59 times the minimum." From my my own observations, detailed

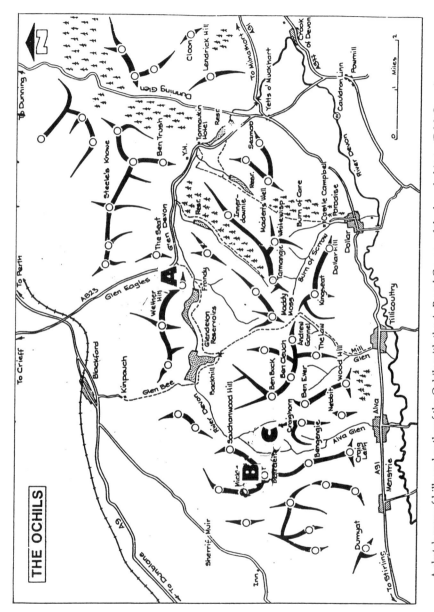

A sketch map of hills and paths of the Ochils with the A, B and C areas of the hare habitats. (R McOwan)

below, I consider that mountain hare numbers reached a peak in the Ochil Hills in the mid-1970s and that a most definite decline has occurred since then.

My earliest notes on mountain hares in the Ochils were short and infrequent – e.g. "10-4-1964 Hare droppings at cairn at Whitewisp Hill but saw no hares. Fox scats here and there on Whitewisp and Tarmangie Hills; 18-4-1964 Blue hare on Ben Cleuch side of King's Seat Hill; 31-1-1965 Mountain hare, rather dingy grey but in winter coat, ran off as I walked across snow-covered moss from Blairdenon Hill towards Ben Cleuch; 10-5-1965 Single mountain hare, very grey and fawn, near top of The Law."

These results show that in the mid-1960s these hares were indeed scarce, certainly on the grassier hills and even on the heathery mosses. Numbers however increased very rapidly and in the early 1970s I became accustomed to seeing the hares quite low down in considerable numbers, not only in favoured habitat such as heather moors on the east side of the Blackford-Sheriff Muir road, but also in poor areas such as the low grassy hills adjoining the Dunning-Path of Condie road. During a high-level walk over all the Ochil 610m heights on 13-4-1971 we traversed from Sheriff Muir road over Greenforet Hill and finished up on Innerdownie. My notes at that time include "Mountain hares plentiful everywhere from Sheriff Muir road over the heathery moor on Black Hill where 36 actually seen, quite brown in coat colour, fewer high up on Blairdenon (where it is quite grassy) but these whiter. Common among eroded peat islands and heather/crowberry moor and peat hags between Blairdenon Hill and Ben Buck, but very scarce from there eastwards – probably not enough heather." We must have seen more than 100 hares that day but unfortunately the long distance involved in the day's walk cut down time for counting and note-taking, regrettable though this seems in retrospect.

The highest number I actually counted in the Ochils was on 30-3-1975, when a walk over Area B and Alva Moss gave a total of 66. This would be a minimum however because a few almost certainly must have been missed amongst the innumerable hags. Numbers have declined sharply since then, as Table 1 reveals. I have excluded from the table results from King's Seat, Tarmangie and Whitewisp Hills as the highest number seen other than in the main areas was 6 on King's Seat Hill on 4-3-1973.

The best time of year to count the species is in winter or early spring if the hills are clear of snow and the animals are either in their white winter coat (Figure 1) or retain sufficient of it to be easily spotted. For most of the year mountain hares are active mainly by night. During the day, except in times of food shortage such as in winters with deep and prolonged snow-lie, they rest either on seats or pads at the entrance to burrows which they dig in peat banks, or squat in forms which they carve out in heather or amongst rushes or grasses. In these forms they are virtually invisible when in their brown summer and autumn coats and a searcher can unknowingly pass them by if they remain crouched. In winter and early spring the white tops of their heads can be picked out quite easily in the forms with binoculars even at several hundred

Figure 1. A very white mountain hare at 800m altitude on the Cairngorms. Only 1% of Scottish mountain hares turn as white as this in winter.

Figure 2. A white hare caught napping in early spring in a sunny hollow in the heather. In this position the ears are flattened to help concealment.

metres distance, always provided that there is little or no snow (Figure 2).

While it is difficult to be certain whether mountain hares are completely absent from a previously occupied area, their presence can be verified by several clues even though the animals are not seen. The hares tend to follow well made tracks through heather or grass and their dry droppings can be spotted on these tracks, or on areas where they have been grazing. No mammalian enzymes can digest cellulose and some other carbohydrates but bacterial enzymes can and in certain mammals, especially those possessing a rumen or large caecum, bacterial digestion of these carbohydrates makes a large contribution to the animals' nutrition (Smith et al 1983). To benefit from this however, hares, like all lagomorphs, have to carry out reingestion or refection, i.e. they pass food twice through their alimentary canal. The first time they produce soft mucus-coated faeces which they catch directly from their anus and re-ingest. The process is called caecotrophy and the soft droppings are caecotrophs (Young 1981) which are formed in the caecum. Schmidt-Nielsen (1983) who gives a good brief account calls it coprophagy. In addition to other substances the caecotrophs are said to contain bacterial-produced vitamims essential for the good health of the lagomorphs (Matthews 1971). The second time through, hard dry fibrous droppings are produced and these, with experience, are readily distinguished from rabbit droppings and old dry sheep droppings.

Another helpful piece of evidence is the presence in spring of patches of moulted white winter fur, which is very different from sheep's wool. Mountain hares undergo three colour changes during the year, wearing a mostly white coat in winter (Figure 3), a brown coat in summer and another brownish coat in autumn, which is replaced by the white winter pelage partly by a moult and partly by a blanching of existing black or brown hairs. Also, where hares are plentiful, dead hares or skeletons are frequently found. Foxes are a main predator on mountain hares and examination of their scats (droppings) can often reveal hare fur. Foxes however appear to hunt less frequently on the higher reaches of the Ochils nowadays, if one may judge from their scats being much scarcer than formerly in the areas I have searched. The golden eagle is another chief predator on mountain hares farther north, in the Highlands, where I have observed hare carcasses in eyries; but the eagles' influence on the Ochil Hills is negligible – in 31 years I have seen a total of only 3 golden eagles in the range. The stoat is a possible predator, its footprints being frequently seen in the snow in winter on the high plateaus, and I have watched a stoat chasing a mountain hare on Choinneachain Hill though I did not see the outcome.

Table 1 shows that a decline in mountain hare numbers has occurred since about 1980/81. Shooting may have been partly responsible but this cannot be the whole answer. Poor weather is frequently a factor in population fluctuations, e.g. with the red grouse *Lagopus lagopus scoticus* which in 1993 suffered such a drastic reduction in numbers on many moors that shooting had to be cancelled. This was caused by snowfalls in May followed by heavy rain

Date	Area A	Alva Moss	Area C
13-4-71		Common	Plentiful
14-11-74	14		
30-3-75		44+	20+
2-5-76	25		
17-9-77	2		
7-1-78	12		
16-4-79			numerous
11-1-81	22		
18-4-81			3
18-4-82			none
1983	none		footprints of 1 only
21-10-84			none
1985	3	1	
1986	no signs		1, plus 2 sets tracks in snow
1987	no signs	6 fresh droppings	fox scats with hare fur
24-2-88	no signs		1 set tracks in snow
1990/1991	no signs		no signs
1992	1 dropping		1; many tracks in snow
31-1-93	1 seen		
9-5-93	2 droppings 0.5km apart		
11-5-93		droppings in 4 places; 1 burrow in use	

Table 1. Observations on the Scottish mountain hare in the western section of the Ochil Hills. Where a year date only is given, this means that result; for several different days that year have been lumped together, while blanks indicate either no visit or no notes on hares.

in June, resulting in poor breeding. But bad weather is unlikely to have greatly affected the Ochils Hares. The nearby Campsie Fells endure similar weather to the Ochils, but during a five miles walk on the western Campsies in February 1992 with the naturalist T. D. H. Merrie we saw more than a dozen white hares, so there has been no decline there.

Inter-specific competition is another factor affecting populations. The preferred diet of mountain hares is pioneer heather, i.e. young heather growth, and this is normally obtained by muirburn in spring. The heather in the three main areas described is all old, not having been burned for many years, and consequently must contain little nutrition. The main competitors of mountain hares for heather are the red grouse and domestic sheep *Ovis aries*, but red grouse are very scarce both in Area B where there is little heather and on Alva Moss where the heather is in very poor condition. The heather in Area A is much better and a few grouse are still shot there annually. The sheep I have seen in the Ochils feed mainly on grass and apparently graze little on the heather, crowberry *Empetrum nigrum* or blaeberry, so it is unlikely that sheep affect hare numbers there. Parasites and diseases form yet another factor, but I have no knowledge of how these may have influenced hares in the Ochils.

Cyclic fluctuations are well known in voles, lemmings and other mammals, as well as in birds, insects and fishes. A classic example, often quoted (e.g. by Odum 1971) shows a 9 to 10 year periodicity in the snowshoe hare *Lepus americanus*. But as regards the mountain hare Hewson (in Corbet and Harris 1991) states "Peak numbers may occus at c10 year intervals in Scotland but there is no firm evidence that these are cyclical." He considers that "Food shortage is the likeliest proximate factor in population crashes." I believe this to be the case in the Ochils, where optimum hare habitat is very patchy.

Study of Table 1 will show that if an approximately 10 year cycle applied in the Ochils, then numbers should have built up again by about 1990, but this did not materialise. It should be realised that often there is no easy answer, or even general agreement, as to what causes population fluctuations and cycles. The red grouse has undergone more study than any other species in Scotland, but even today there are two main and very different theories about the causes of red grouse cycles. One, based on research by the Game Conservancy, holds that the cycles are chiefly caused by parasites and diseases (Hudson 1986, 1992). The other arises from work carried out over many years by a research team of the Instutite of Terrestrial Ecology at Banchory. Their results, published in many papers, are condensed by Wynne-Edwards (1986). The ITE team concluded that red grouse regulate their own numbers by their behaviour, which alters according to the changing quality and carrying capacity of the food supply.

It will be interesting to see if the mountain hare population in the Ochil Hills makes a recovery, and how long this takes. One can only hope that some future researcher will be sufficiently interested to find out.

References and Further Reading

Corbett, G. B. and Harris, S. (Editors). 1991. The Handbook of British Mammals, 3rd Edition. Blackwell Scientific Publications, Oxford.

Corbett, L et al. 1994. Central Scotland – land, wildlife, people. Forth Naturalist and Historian. Stirling University.

Flux, J. E. C. 1970. Life History of the Mountain Hare (*Lepus timidus scoticus*) in north-east Scotland. *Journal of Zoology*. 161, 75-123. London.

Hudson P. 1986. Red Grouse, the biology and management of a wild gamebird. The Game Conservancy Trust, Fordingbridge.

Hudson, P. 1992. Grouse in Space and Time. The population biology of a managed gamebird. Game Conservancy Limited, Fordingbridge.

Matthews, L. H. 1971. The Life of Mammals. Volume 2. Weidenfeld and Nicolson, London.

Odum, E. P. 1971. Fundamentals of Ecology, 3rd Edition. W. B. Saunders Company, Philadelphia.

Rintoul, L. J. and Baxter, E. V. 1935. A Vertebrate Fauna of Forth. Oliver and Boyd, Edinburgh.

Ritchie, J. 1920. The Influence of Man on Animal Life in Scotland. Cambridge University Press.

Schmidt-Nielsen, K. 1983. Animal Physiology: Adaptation and Environment, 3rd Edition. Cambridge University Press.

Smith, E. L., Hill, R. L., Lehman, I. R., Lefkowitz, R. J., Handler, P. & White, A. 1983. Principles of Biochemistry: Mammalian Biochemistry, 7th Edition. McGraw-Hill, London.

Timms, D. W. G. (Editor). 1974. The Stirling Region. Stirling University.

Wynne-Edwards, V. C. 1986. Evolution through Group Selection. Blackwell Scientific Publications, Oxford.

Young, J. Z. 1981. The Life of Vertebrates, 3rd Edition. Clarendon Press, Oxford.

Figure 3. Mountain hare in winter coat, with ears pricking up as it alerts at approach of photographer. Note black on ears, brown nose and off-white colour of face.

CLACKMANNAN RIVER CORRIDORS SURVEY

Cathy Tilbrook
Scottish Natural Heritage

BACKGROUND

Within Clackmannan District there are two main river systems - the Devon and the Black Devon (see Map). With a combined length of some 70km, these two systems flow through a large area of the District and as such represent an important wildlife and recreational resource for local communities. However, like many other British rivers, the two rivers and their associated wildlife habitats are under threat from piecemeal planning applications, water pollution and habitat destruction.

Scottish Natural Heritage (SNH), along with many local people and organisations, was concerned about these trends and identified a need for more comprehensive information on the river systems to help decision makers to formulate a more strategic approach to land use planning and habitat improvement works. It was therefore decided to commission a survey, to be funded by SNH and Central Regional Council, to provide this background information.

OBJECTIVES

The aims of the survey were to:

1. Gather detailed information on the physical, biological and landscape features of the two rivers and their adjacent habitats through field survey work, also identifying areas of human activity.

2. Analyse the data collected to:

   - identify areas of importance for various interests (including nature conservation, landscape, access and recreation), and

   - identify areas where human activities are posing a threat to the quality of the rivers.

INITIAL STAGE

Preliminary work was carried out to identify riparian land ownership and collate background information. Other organisations were consulted for details such as water quality data and designations applying to the rivers, and sources such as Central Scotland and the *Forth Naturalist and Historian* (1994 and 1975-) were searched for historical information and details of past surveys. Although much work has been done on the rivers, no attempt appears to have been made previously to collate all the information in a systematic way.

At this stage, land owners and occupiers were approached for permission

Map – The Rivers Devon and Black Devon – Clackmannan District Area – from Bartholemew's Central Scotland (1:100,000) at 85%.

for access to their land, and some publicity was sought to explain the project to local people. We are grateful to all those who gave access permission for this work to be completed.

FIELDWORK

The fieldwork itself was carried out at the end of July by Ecosurveys, a company with great experience in carrying out river corridor surveys throughout Britain. The methodology used was based on a standard technique used by the National Rivers Authority (1992/93) and many other conservation bodies, which makes it easier to compare the Clackmannan Rivers with others and thus put them in a national context. The project was also designed to be compatible with SERCON, a new river evaluation database which is currently being developed by a team of specialists from throughout Britain.

In the field, the surveyors walked along the river banks and used sections of large-scale maps to record physical characteristics, vegetation and notes on wildlife observed. Details on adjacent landuses, developments and pollution sources were also mapped, as well as descriptions of landscape character and access and recreational use. The surveyors were asked to make special note of features such as signs of use by otter and areas of interesting wet-dependent habitat, such as marsh, ox-bow and fen.

FUTURE PLANS

Work on completing the report is now underway. This will provide a section-by section description of the characteristics of the two rivers, and an overall summary document to put each stretch into context and identify areas of high and low quality for different features. Once this information is available, it is hoped that the results can be discussed with landowners, planners and other interested bodies to attempt to achieve a more integrated approach to the management of the river corridor areas. An example of potential benefit is in the planning of flood prevention works, which can be much more effective and less harmful to wildlife if tackled in a more strategic way.

If sufficient interest arises from discussion of the survey results, then it may be possible to re-instate the River Devon Trust, an idea raised some years ago, which was never formalised.

Anyone who wishes to discuss this project in more detail, or who considers they may have background information of interest to us on either the Devon or Black Devon rivers, please contact the author – Clackmannan District Officer, SNH.

REFERENCES

Central Scotland – land, wildlife, people. 1994. L. Corbett et al. Forth Naturalist and Historian, Stirling University.
Forth Naturalist and Historian, annually 1975-. Forth Naturalist and Historian, Stirling University.

National Rivers Authority. 1992. River Corridor Surveys. *Conservation Technical Handbook No. 1.* NRA, Bristol.
National Rivers Authority. 1993. River Landscape Assessment. *Conservation Technical Handbook No. 2.* NRA, Bristol.

River Devon – looking west.

BOOK REVIEWS AND NOTES (Naturalist)

A SHORE FUTURE: vision for the coast; save our shorebirds campaign. 40pp. RSPB. £5.

Our coastline is a priceless asset for people and wildlife alike. Millions of the world's birds depend on it for nesting, as winter homes, and for places to rest on migration. Ill conceived development and other uses now threaten many habitats. Wildlife on the coasts must have help and consideration from people if it is to thrive. Historically man's attitude to estuaries has been one of disdain – with industry hideously disfiguring, saltmarshes and mudflats reclaimed by agriculture – and continues today with, for example, an arrogant government about to sanction the destruction of an entire estuarine complex in Cardiff for purely cosmetic purposes; environmental vandalism ignoring planning policy and international responsibilities for wildlife.

This A4 book is nicely illustrated with plates and figures, and RSPB's recommendations (pp6-7) detail the need for a national strategy to develop integrated management of the coastal zone; involving discrete units of government environment, National River Authority, environmental protection agencies, local and regional authorities. A separate four-page leaflet illustrates 12 habitat watching areas of the coasts of south and west Scotland including the Forth.

L. C.

ANCIENT WOODLAND IN SCOTLAND. Scottish Natural Heritage. Nov. 1993. 16pp.

Handsomely produced in colour on environmentally friendly paper this booklet assures us of SNH's recognition of the unique value of natural woodland, now just 1% of our land surface. The recently completed *Inventory of Ancient, Long-Established and semi-Natural Woodland* is a major source for correction, planning and forestry, to act restoringly to amend today's gloomy picture of our little remaining natural woodland. SNH hopes in reading this booklet people come to appreciate its beauty and value, are inspired to visit some of these woods protected as nature reserves, and to play an active role in the conservation of our vanishing ancient woodland.

L. C.

WALKER'S COMPANION – SCOTLAND. R. McOwen, H. Brown and R. Mearns. Ward Lock (Cassell). 1994. £7.99.

Rennie notes to me that this is a new pocket-sized issue of the book initially titled *Great Walks – Scotland*, hardback 1989 and softback 1991.

THE SCOTTISH NATURALIST

The following are selected as of FN&H interest from the years 1988-1994 just recently received because of printing delays.

1994

Ten years of Population Counts of Orchids at Dumbrock, Loch Meadows, Stirlingshire, and Problems of Management – C. A. Dickson and W. Parkes. 22 (4), 349-360.

The Inchlonaig Yews, their Tree Epiphytes, and their Tree Partners. Pilkington, Proctor and Reid. 365-373.

1993

Loch Ness Bathymetric and Seismic Survey. Dec. 1991.

Apart from the pioneer work of Murray and Pullar 100 years ago scientific study of the loch remained rather neglected till Peter Maitland's multi-disciplined survey of 1977-80 (*Ecology of Scotland's Largest Lochs*) – the definitive background for further studies. 200,000 soundings were made in the five days of this 1991 December survey with modern sonar equipment, and with datum transposed to the level used by Murray and Pullar charts plotted to allow comparison, results show a positive similarity. Maximum depths in North and South Basins being just 3 and 4m less than the 1903 figures of 230m and 225m respectively.

1992

Charcoal Burners' Platforms in West Scotland – Rennie pp51-111.

Romans and Strathclyde – the Road System pt 5 – Loudon Hill to the Highland Boundary Fault Frontier – Newell and Lorie pp7-47.

1990

The Lake of Menteith: Aspects of its Ecology – Fozzard and Marsden – survey and work by FRPB in 1981-5. pp57-129.

Breeding Passerine Communities of Duneland Habitats in NE Fife – Earlshallmuir and Tentsmuir – Dougall pp53-93.

Roman Road System pts 1&2 – General and the Western flank of the Antonine Frontier –Newell and Lorie pp3-49.

1989

The Influence of Alexander Wilson on John James Audubon-Hunter pp85-95.

First Record of Lesser Rorquel (whale) in Dunbartonshire – Gibson pp97-100.

1988

Symposium Proceedings: the Search for Nessie in the 1980s. Royal Museum of Scotland, 25 July 1987. Editors Gibson and Heppell. 180pp.

NORWAY AND SCOTLAND: a study in land use. Reforesting Scotland. Ullapool. 24pp. 1993. Charities £4.50. Government/Commercial £12.50.

This full-colour illustrated booklet presents challenging ideas and provocative questions about the future of land use in rural Scotland based on the experience of a Study Tour by 31 people representing appropriate organisations. Nine days were spent touring and studying in Hordaland, western Norway, to see what lessons can be learnt about land use and ownership from the economically and socially thriving Norwegian landscape.

PROTECTING OUR ENVIRONMENT: a citizens' guide to environmental rights and action in Scotland. Friends of the Earth Scotland, 70-72 Newhaven Road, Edinburgh EH6 5QG. £4.95

Authors/Reviewers Addresses

Corbett, L., 30 Dunmar Drive, Alloa FK10 2EH.

Corner, R. W. M., Hawthorn Hill, 36 Wordsworth Street, Penrith CA11 7QZ.

Follett, G. F., 5 White Dales, Edinburgh EH10 7JQ.

Harrison, S. J., Environmental Services, University of Stirling.

Henty, C. J., Dept. of Psychology, University of Stirling.

Jackson, Brian, National Museum of Scotland, Geology Dept., Chambers Street, Edinburgh EH1 1JF.

Knowler, John T., see Mitchell.

Low, Donald, 17 Charlton Road, Bridge of Allan.

Main, Lorna, Central Region, Viewforth, Stirling.

Maxwell-Irving, Alastair, Telford House, Blairlogie FK9 5PZ.

Millar, Gavin, 4 Carlie Avenue, Bridge of Allan FK9 4JH.

Mitchell, John, 22 Muirpark Way, Drymen G63 0GX.

Page, R., Kingarth, Airthrey Road, Stirling FK9 5PH.

Seaman, Alastair, Eamonn Wall, 22 West Burnside, Dollar FK14 7DP.

Sharp, James, 23 Slandalane House, Kincardine FK10 4NZ.

Stott, Louis, Creag Darach, Milton-of-Aberfoyle FK8 3TD.

Stewart, Isobel G., 16 Kellie Place, Alloa.

Tewnion, Alex, 14 Mylne Avenue, Dollar FK14 7HS.

Thomson, George, 2 Ravenhill, Lochmaben, DG11 1QZ.

Tilbrook, Cathy, Scottish Natural Heritage, Beta Centre, Information Park, University of Stirling.

NEW LIGHT ON STEVENSON

Louis Stott

Consumer resistance to even lavishly illustrated volumes at more than £20 is well enough known to booksellers. With the publication of the first volumes of the *Letters of Robert Louis Stevenson* edited by Ernest Mehew one, or one's Public Library, perhaps, is being invited to embark on the purchase of eight volumes at 5p short of £30 each, and, with Vikhram Seth's thousand-page literary blockbuster, *A Suitable Boy*, available in paperback at £8.99, and Penguin Popular Classics costing £1, one might be prompted to ask whether it is going to be worth it: the answer is a resounding 'yes'.

It is a particular treat in his centenary year to have ready access to fresh chunks of Stevenson's prose. We have long known how illuminating his letters could be, even in the expurgated form we have had access to them in the *Tusitala* edition. Sidney Colvin, the editor of that edition eventually married Fanny Sitwell with whom the young Stevenson was infatuated. The young author poured his heart out to her in his letters and, unsurprisingly, Colvin amended these letters in various ways, even joining one to another and, sometimes, getting the order wrong. The chief general interest in the first two volumes is probably in having these letters in full. Although the intriguing questions which there are about this relationship are still there, we now have a fuller, more honest version of it.

There are three critical holiday summers in Scotland to come in later volumes, but we already have, in volumes one and two, Stevenson, the Scot. It is salutary, perhaps, to note that these two volumes are, also, decidedly 'French'. Menton is bulked out, as are Paris and Barbizon: these letters illuminate both of these periods. It can be noted, too, that the manuscripts of many of the unpublished letters in the first two volumes are in the National Library of Scotland. There is more detail, but there are no particular grounds for a qualitative change in our assessment of RLS. For example, there is a fine metaphor in an unpublished letter to Ferrier, killed young by the demon drink: "... always keep the head to the wind with a little work". To Bob Stevenson he writes, at 21, "I want an object, a mission, a belief, a hope to be my wife". He complains later on in the same letter about Scotland. The stunning openness of his correspondence is fully revealed by the publication in full of many letters, in particular, to Mrs Sitwell, but the picture we already have of him is a relatively sound one. For example, he honestly tells her about a close encounter with a prostitute in Portobello, but he leaves the money and runs. Equally we have him limping home from Portobello having missed the train. This does not alter what we already know or can imagine, but the picture is magnificently embellished.

The letters can, of course, be read on their own account, and make a good place to start on this multi-faceted personality without reference to the 'literature', although there will be those who believe that the importance of Stevenson's work has already been obscured because of what we think we know about him, and argue that the novels and stories and the essays and poems should be read first.

More than 800 pages into these letters RLS is a twenty-eight year old upper-middle class Scotsman with ambitions to be a writer whose first really successful book, *Travels With a Donkey*, has only just been published. He is on the threshold of leaving Scotland, never to live there permanently again. Yet he is a Scottish author whose language, and whose points of reference are firmly rooted in his native land. By the end of the second volume he has met Fanny Osbourne and is on the point of going half way across the world to marry her. There are key visits to Scotland to come, but Stevenson is henceforth a visitor.

There is thus great significance in having the fullest possible account of the origins of his lifelong love affair with his native land, and with the character of its people: "... five square feet of Scottish hillside would take a man a lifetime to describe, and even then how lame, how empty ...," he writes to his cousin Bob, when he was just eighteen. This long unpublished letter contains the substantial topographical essay *Night Outside The Wick Mail*, and the same volume also has, for example, the considerable *Orkney and Shetland Journal* as well as many other shorter letters, some of which are almost 'one-liners', culled from sale catalogues. Then there are such things as inscriptions to his mother and his nurse in *An Inland Voyage*, and brief letters to publishers acknowledging cheques, or seeking responses. Indeed young authors can take comfort from a succession of letters from RLS to John Blackwood (whose silence becomes evident), as he plaintively asks for the return of a manuscript while still leaving open the possibility that Blackwood may publish it. If previous editors have thought fit to omit or overlook some of these elegantly and sometimes wittily expressed trifles what we now have are many more of the building blocks of Stevenson's career as a writer: the agony when a piece is not published, or can't be got right; the delight when work is accepted.

Stevenson's associations with the Stirling District have been ably and lovingly dealt with by the literary topographer who wrote *The Misty Isle of Skye*, Canon John A. MacCulloch; by two Town Clerks of Stirling, Alexander Morrison and David B. Morris; and, more recently, in both *The Forth Naturalist and Historian* and *The Scots Magazine*, by David Angus. It remains difficult to assess the influence which these boyhood/early adult associations with the district had on Stevenson. It can be argued that a dozen visits to the district by the young Edinburgh lad sowed in him an abiding fascination with the Highlands, and gave him material which he used in his best novels. The district certainly surfaced in later letters, and, very specifically, in *Notes of Childhood* (1873), in *Memoir of Himself* (1899), and in *Rosa Quo Locorum* (1893). There are specific poems in *A Child's Garden of Verses*: the delightful *From a Railway Carriage*, as well as *A Good Boy*, and other poems. David Morris's splendid book showed convincingly that Stevenson's considerable knowledge of the Jacobites must have originated in the Stirling District.

Of particular local interest in the first two volumes, the letter (from Edinburgh) already referred to also contains a description of a walk he and his cousin Bob had taken up the Allan:

"Lying here in my bed, I have been brooding over past walks. Especially our walk up the Allan, – you remember it? And how after having passed all the wooden banks, we came out past a cavern on a bit of river-meadow 'edged with Poplar pale', surrounded on three sides by the retiring and then re-advancing wooded banks, and on the fourth by the brawling river and high ground on the further side. We passed through the meadow and came to a road betwixt two walls and two woods that sloped up the hillside precisely after the fashion of 'the straight and narrow way' between the Interpreter's house and Beelzebub's garden, in our delightful edition of the delightful book. Only one fault have I to find with the artist's conception: it is too much of a 'deadman's lane', fitter for a bloody robbery than the trashy surfeit of apples, British cholera and pill-boxes with which it is connected in the text. But where I chiefly long to be is at the immediate exit from the wood, where the river splashes through some rapids dewing with spray the overhanging trees, and you see it bearing away its taches of foam in a slow brown stream between 'the nodding horror of two shady brows'."

The density of allusion and description in this paragraph suggest what riches there are in these books. The well-read (with sufficient recall) will pick up two distinct references to Milton, and one to Pilgrim's Progress. The present Editor, Ernest Mehew, points these out. He also draws attention to another, already published, letter describing the same walk, tells us that RLS had received a three-volume edition of Milton for his eighteenth birthday, and that he possessed a copiously illustrated *Pilgrim's Progress*, about which he later wrote in the *Magazine of Art*.

Mehew's knowledge of Stevenson, and his era is encyclopaedic and, in him, Stevenson has at last found a Boswell worthy of him. He is, for example, a secure guide to such arcane expressions as 'pock-pudding', and points out that, when Stevenson refers to "the Retreating Denizen of the Pays Bas", the Carl Rosa Opera Company were in Edinburgh performing 'The Flying Dutchman'.

RLS's mother, his wife, his step-son and one of his best friends, for one reason and another, destroyed or distorted what Stevenson, the correspondent, had to say. For example, we know from the essay, *Old Mortality*, that RLS watched a gravedigger "in the red evening, high above Allan Water and in the shadow of Dunblane Cathedral", and wrote of "the poetry of the profession" of gravedigger. It is disappointing, because it might have contained a morsel which illuminated this passage, to know that his mother destroyed one of his letters from Dunblane because she considered it morbid.

In so far as he has been able to, Mehew has re-constructed the letters, 2800 of which are to be published. His introduction and his headnotes, brief where appropriate, more elaborate where necessary (as for the meeting at Grezs of RLS and his future wife), are masterly exercises in biography, measured and objective, but opinionated too. Indeed, in these first two volumes Mehew is emerging as a character in his own right: "Amidst much dross ..." he begins, reviewing some previous work; elsewhere he points out more gently that Jenni Calder misdates a letter, but acknowledges the value of her contributions to Stevenson scholarship.

Stevenson's Bridge of Allan and Dunblane periods are well enough treated in the *Tusitala* edition, and there are no surprises in the new edition of the Letters, but there is new material. Apart from the letter already referred to there is a 'joke' letter to his father from Darnley House, Bridge of Allan at age 16, a reference to some poetry (three lines) about the Allan in a notebook at Yale, and an unpublished Christmas Day letter from Bridge of Allan in 1872 ("... everyone explains my stay here as having reference to some unknown 'young lady' in 'one of the villas'."). Two more considerable letters describe the Jaffray sisters, and Andrew Manson, photographer of Bridge of Allan, and praise "that great wall of the Ochils" and Blairlogie. There is, too, a brief coded message to Fanny Sitwell from the Queens Hotel.

With regard to the rest of Scotland, apart from Edinburgh and its vicinity, Helensburgh and Leven, both places where there were Balfour relatives, play a part which they were not granted by Colvin. There is more detail too, but nothing particularly revealing, about his trip in the yacht Heron and to Attadale. All in all, the letters in the first two volumes substantially enlarge what we already know about Stevenson, and they will take a long time to digest. He emerges sometimes as more mature when letters which have been sanitised are available in full, but he is still the same enigma who we believe we understand at one moment, and then discover, at the next, that we still have not got the measure of.

Yale are to be congratulated on this project. They might have used better paper for the photographs, and they might have shown more imagination in some of the setting (the *Tusitala* edition looks better), but these are only minor infringements of the commandments. Yale should have made it plain, too, that Ernest Mehew is the sole editor of the Letters. However, the first two volumes are very good, and the best, the more mature Stevenson, is yet to come.

MEHEW, Ernest and Bradford BOOTH, Editors. The Letters of Robert Louis Stevenson. Volume 1 1854-April 1874, 525pp, and 2 April 1874-July 1879, 355pp. Yale University Press. 1994, each volume £29.95.

References

COLVIN, Sir Sidney. The Letters of Robert Louis Stevenson, Tusitala Edition. Heinemann, 1924.

MacCULLOCH, John A. Stevenson and Bridge of Allan. John Smith, Glasgow, 1927.

MORRIS, David B. Robert Louis Stevenson and the Scottish Highlanders. Aeneas Mackay, Stirling, 1929.

MORRISON, Alexander, RLS's ancestral, personal and literary associations with Bridge of Allan. Learmonth, 1932. Reprint of paper read to, and in the *Transactions of the Stirling Natural History and Archaeological Society*. 25 January 1932.

ROBERT LOUIS STEVENSON AND FRANCE

Robert Louis Stevenson's stepson Lloyd Osbourne observes in an introduction to *New Arabian Nights*,

"France had a profound influence over Stevenson; mentally he was half a Frenchman; in taste, habits, and prepossessions he was almost wholly French. Not only did he speak French admirably and read it like his mother-tongue, but he loved both country and people, and was more really at home in France than anywhere else."

Louis Stott's *Robert Louis Stevenson & France* (Creag Darach Publications, 1994, Aberfoyle £6.99, ISBN 1-874585-03-2) is a richly informative treatment of its subject, which deserves to be consulted long after the centenary of Stevenson's death is past. An attractively illustrated book of 127 pages, it contains a lively Introduction and 10 chapters on such diverse and key subjects as 'RLS And Scottish And French Art', 'The Inland Voyage', and 'Stevenson In France: Fontainebleau'. In addition, Mr Stott's 'Gazeteer of Literary Sites in France Associated With RLS' is of direct help to any traveller whose literary curiosity has been awakened, while 'On The Trail of Stevenson In France' supplies an itinerary, with the friendly practical tip ' It is a crowded schedule, and will be found tiring if undertaken in fourteen days". *Robert Louis Stevenson & France* is warmly recommended.

Donald A. Low

STEVENSON ESSAYS OF LOCAL INTEREST

Travelling Hopefully and The Breck Trek are two of the 30 essays on Stevenson in the recent *Robert Louis Stevenson – Bright Ring of Words* edited by Alanna Knight and Elizabeth Warfel, Balnain £12.99. These two six page essays are by local authors. The first by David Angus, sadly lost to us last January, is on his special interest in Stevenson and particularly associations with Bridge of Allan. The second is by Rennie McOwan. Rennie's is an interesting study on the route of David Balfour and Alan Breck from shipwreck off Mull across central Scotland to Corstorphine Hill and Queensferry in Stevenson's *Kidnapped*. Rennie also refers to the Stevenson family climbing Dumyat which David Angus mentions in his *FN&H* paper RLS at Bridge of Allan, which is now available as a pamphlet at £1.

Stevenson features in two other pamphlets based on *FN&H* papers, Robert Louis Stevenson and the Trossachs by Louis Stott at 80p, and The Royal Hunt of a Lion – Charles Dickens at Bridge of Allan by David Angus at 60p.

BRIDGE OF ALLAN:
A HERITAGE OF MUSIC, AND ITS MUSEUM HALL

Gavin Millar and George McVicar

In April 1994 George McVicar, well known local musician and one time vice-Chairman of the Bridge of Allan Music Club, gave the annual Dr Welsh Bridge of Allan Educational and Historical Trust lecture "A Musician remembers". While based on reminiscences of the many famous musicians who performed in Bridge of Allan's Museum Hall under the auspices of Music Club, he also documented the earlier successful Public Interests Association concerts. Mr McVicar came to this area in 1956 and has a long and distinguished career in music.

"There is a great deal I remember, although of course I have no recollection of Chopin's visit to Keir House in 1848. In all the biographies of the composer, Jane Stirling's name is immortalised, at least in musical circles."

Chopin composed the Nocturne (opus 55 no. 1) to 'Mlle à J. W. Stirling', and the piano he played was till recently preserved at Keir. He was in poor health while in Scotland, and only played two concerts. The Glasgow one in Merchants' Hall was impressive to the critics, but virtually half empty. According to legend Jane Stirling, fearing a similar situation in Hopetoun Rooms, Edinburgh, bought one hundred tickets for herself and friends. In 1849 Chopin was very ill indeed in Paris; Jane Stirling sent him £1,000, but he was dying then. Following Chopin and on through the 20th century Bridge of Allan has attracted many of the world's great musicians.

"I would first like to make reference to the rated pianist Frederick Lamond; he lived in Bridge of Allan for the last eighteen months of his life and died in Stirling during 1948. His death wish was to hear the last Beethoven Quartets. I met him twice, while I was a student at the Scottish National Academy of Music (now the RSAMD) where Lamond taught. On one occasion, I met him in a corridor at the Academy – he looked very upset and explained to me 'I'm Lamond and I'm lost!'. The next time I met him in his studio. I had been told he was not coming in so I was making use of the piano in his room, when he unexpectedly arrived and said profoundly 'You have taken my piano!'

I know of no other of the world's great composers who visited Bridge of Allan. Mendelssohn came to Scotland and Robert Burns visited Stirling and Clackmannanshire. I mention Burns, to whom the traditional music of Scotland owes an unparalled debt. He gloried in the richness of our native folk songs and wrote to Mrs McLehose 'I have collected, begged, borrowed and stolen all the songs I could meet with', and 'this, as you will know, is a task much to my taste'.

It was not only songs Burns collected but also fiddle and pipe tunes, and he wrote words for them or, in other cases, altered and improved existing words.

Maurice Lindsay reckons that but for Burns, 370 traditional Scottish tunes would have been lost. I make no apology for this apparent digression. Far too little notice is taken of the musical side of Burns's genius. Somebody once asked 'what would the world be like without Mozart?' What, however, would the music of Scotland be like without Burns?

But to return to Bridge of Allan. Around 1840, the Music Hall was built in Fountain Road – then known as Market Street – on the site where today's Post Office stands. I expect the hall was used for purposes other than music but we do know that there were concerts held there by the Spa Lodge of the Independent Order of Good Templars between 1894 and 1902. That we have no recollection of them need not distress us because John MacKay in his hand-written notes on 'Music' describes them as 'nothing spectacular'. Earlier concerts in the Nineteenth Century were organised by Bridge of Allan's famous Victorian apothecary and publicist Gilbert Farie. Well, if those concerts organised by the Independent Order of Good Templars were 'nothing spectacular', those of the Public Interests Association (PIA) were very spectacular indeed. The PIA celebrity concerts were held in the Museum Hall and ran from 1905 until 1935. They took place monthly and a season ticket cost £1 5s. To read the list of artists who performed there would do justice to any large city. From now on the talk takes its inspiration, if that is the right word, from Leporello's Catalogue aria in Don Giovanni. Here is the catalogue:

The PIA brought to the Museum Hall – the great pre-war trio of Thibaud, Casals and Cortot; Suggia with Arthur Rubenstein; Suggia again, with Egon Petri; Myra Hess and Irene Scharrer playing two pianos; Elizabeth Schumann with Jaques Thibaud in the same concert. Elizabeth Schumann, again, accompanied by Schnabel; and Sir Donald Tovey, in January 1923. He was Reid Professor of Music at Edinburgh University and gave a recital once a year in London. The critics in London said 'other pianists should listen to Tovey and learn how to do it'. He was an exceptional pianist.

The Glasgow Orpheus Choir, under the direction of their conductor Sir Hugh Roberton, came to the Museum Hall three times. The Scottish Orchestra performed there despite the small platform. Maggie Teyte appeared there with Harold Samuel. Dennis Noble, the famous baritone, appeared with Ailie Cullen, the Scottish pianist to whom Glasgow University gave an honorary Doctorate. William Primrose was also accompanied at the celebrity concerts by Ailie Cullen. Dora Labette, John Coates and Plunkett Greene,the last named who wrote the textbook Interpretation of Song, were amongst the many singers who performed there. The French violinist Jelly d'Aranyi appeared more than once at the celebrity concerts. Bessie Spence came to the Museum Hall in 1913. I once played for one of her students – while I was playing, Bessie took my wrist and smacked it – saying 'Handel needs good handling!'. Lionel Tertis came in 1930. Gerald Moore, the accompanist, also came in 1930. He made many appearances at the Museum Hall.

In 1926, came Maurice Ravel. He performed with four other artists; Dorothy Silk, Zino Francescatti, Gerard Hekking and accompanist George Reeves, who also returned to Bridge of Allan many times. Ravel played his own sonatine and duet 'Mother Goose Suite' with George Reeves. The distinguished American Ruth Draper also appeared, courtesy of the PIA.

In 1935, the celebrity concerts ended. The trustees of the Museum Hall were in debt and owed the Electricity board £44. The electricity supply was subsequently cut off. Dr W H Welsh, who was a trustee and also convener of the PIA, later related that a bazaar was held in 1939 'to get things going again'.

With the Second World War over, the Museum Hall became home to the Bridge of Allan and District Music Club. The Music Club was formed by Dr Welsh in 1945 and soon became known for giving concerts of the same high standard of music as the earlier PIA celebrity concerts. Not to be outdone by the Chopin and Keir House of 1848 or indeed by the PIA bringing Ravel in 1926, the Music Club brought Benjamin Britten and Peter Pears to the Allan Water Hotel in 1946. There they performed the Michelangelo sonnets of 1940. Britten and Pears returned in 1949, this time to the Museum Hall, then once more in 1950. The programme says that they performed the Canticle Op 41, but Op 41 is the 'Charm of Lullabies' which Britten wrote for the mezzo-soprano Nancy Evans and I think it may have been Canticle I 'My Beloved is Mine' which is for tenor and piano. The programme also included 'Fish in the unruffled lakes' with the setting of words by Auden. I consider Britten to be the greatest composer who lived his life out completely in the Twentieth Century. I phrased that sentence very carefully. Other great composers, born in the Nineteenth Century, have died in the Twentieth, however, Britten was born and died within the Twentieth Century.

In the catalogue of celebrities who came to the Museum Hall through 'the Club', I am certain to miss out some names that you may remember with special affection. Just before I came to live here you had Moiseiwitsch. Max Rostal and Franz Osborne came in 1947. Phyllis Sellick and her husband, Cyril Smith also came in 1947. In November 1947 Margaret Ritchie appeared along with accompanist Eric Gritton. Campoli was also accompanied by Eric Gritton when he gave violin recitals to the Club in 1948 and 1951. Joan and Valery Trimble were brought to the Museum Hall in 1948, as were Wight Henderson and Herrick Bunney, organist at Saint Giles Cathedral in Edinburgh. The Zephyr Trio, consisting of oboist Evelyn Rothwell (wife of Sir John Barbirolli), flautist Gareth Morris and pianist Wilfrid Parry, appeared in February 1948. The Duo Barbirolli, in which Lady Barbirolli was accompanied by Iris Loveridge on pianoforte, appeared twice for the Music Club, in 1975 and 1981 after the club moved to the MacRobert Centre in 1971.

The Boyd Neel Orchestra came in 1949. Kathleen Ferrier and Gerald Moore came in 1950. She sang twice in the Museum Hall as guest of the Music Club. Winifred Ferrier later gave a talk to the Club about her sister. Musica da Camera appeared in 1951 and again in 1960. The Hirsch String Quartet came in 1952 and again in 1959. Moiseiwitsch returned in 1954 with Elisabeth Schwarzkopf.

Ian Wallace made a number of visits to the Music Club. He has close associations with the district and apparently his mother went to school with that greatly admired personality of the Music Club, Jessie Kerr. Ian Wallace described Jessie as 'a striking example of what a resolute lady can achieve'. She had a marvellous interest in music and was secretary of the Club for many years. Also in 1954 was Eric Roberts String Orchestra. In 1956 came Yonty Solomon, the great South African pianist and the Ballets Minerva. I can take the credit for introducing Alasdair Graham to the Music Club in 1957. He came to a club evening in the Allan Water Hotel and was to return to Bridge of Allan many times with: John Shirley-Quirk in 1965 and 1970; Marte Schlamme, the Viennese singer; he played for Alexander Oliver in 1967; again with Alexander Oliver and the Edinburgh String Quartet in 1968 to perform Vaughan Williams 'On Wenlock Edge'; he accompanied Elisabeth Soderstrom in a recital for the Music Club in 1969. Alasdair is a professor at the Royal College of Music.

Moura Lympany appeared in 1957 and again returns to the MacRobert this year (1994). Fou T'song visited the Music Club in 1959. Janet Baker, the contralto, was accompanied by Margaret Rankin when they visited the Music Club in 1966. The page turner on that occasion was none other than David Frame. I am told when Annie Fischer came, she ordered four eggs for breakfast at the buffet restaurant in Stirling railway station. I also remember Bernadette Greevey, the Irish contralto who came to the Club in October 1971 with Havelock Nelson. We met in the Royal Hotel and she exclaimed, rather philosophically, 'It's a hell of an old life!'. The Julian Bream Consort came in 1963. John Ogdon gave piano recitals to the Club throughout the Sixties.

Stephen Bishop Kovacevich also gave a piano recital of Bach, Stravinsky, Beethoven and Brahms, during 1965. He borrowed a shirt of mine and forgot to return it! The Berlin Philharmonic Octet played a Brahms quintet and an octet by Schubert to the Club in February 1967. As well as Alexander Oliver and Alasdair Graham appearing in March of that year, Robin Fairhurst (baritone) accompanied by Antony Lindsay on pianoforte, gave a recital in November.

Peter Katin became a regular performer at the Music Club. 'Peter is acknowledged as one of the greatest Chopin interpreters of the age', a programme reads. He appeared in 1969, 1972, 1975 and 1980. John Fraser, who is now a Director of EMI, accompanied Margaret Marshall and Geoffrey Lynn at a recital given to the Club in Wallace High School hall in 1974. He also appeared with Alexander Oliver in 1978 and again with Margaret Marshall and Alexander Oliver in February 1983.

Alexander Oliver is of course a tenor and was born in Bridge of Allan. He too has made many visits to the Music Club. Geoffrey Lynn is in the first violin section of the London Symphony Orchestra.

What is striking is that Geoffrey Lynn, Margaret Marshall, Alexander Oliver, David Frame and James Sleigh, the last three being Bridge of Allan men, were all educated at the High School of Stirling. They were pupils of the most exceptional music department in Scotland at the time, run by James S

Melville. It was possibly only rivalled by Kirkcaldy High School. The standards achieved at that time were second to none and those names I have mentioned are proof of that. James Sleigh came to the Music Club in 1984 as part of the Faber Trio. James played viola, Ruth Faber harp and Louise Glanville was flautist. The trio was formed in 1979.

But why have I not spoken more of one man, David Frame? He started as page turner in the Museum Hall and is in the audience tonight. He often played for the Music Club and gave recitals with Donald Maxwell at the Beacon School. David Frame has made a considerable mark on the music of Bridge of Allan. He accompanied Patricia Hay, John Robertson and John Graham in 1972 when they performed for the Club at the MacRobert under the title 'Artists from Scottish Opera'.

Margaret Marshall, as we have already seen, was a regular performer at the Music Club. Kerstin Meyer, the mezzo, gave a recital in February 1970. Wallace High School hall was the venue for a recital by winners of the Music Club prize to the Central Counties Music Festival Association in September 1973. It was also the venue for a recital by senior students of RSAMD in 1976, there was held a recital of piano duets in the same year by Antony Lindsay and Simon Young and in previous years Wallace High School hall was the scene of recitals, by Linda and Gordon Stewart in 1974 and the Roseneathe singers and Roseneathe Orchestra in 1975, all under the auspices of the Bridge of Allan Music Club. I remember Benjamin Luxon, the baritone, with pianist David Willison giving a recital at the MacRobert in 1974.

The BBC Northern Singers and the Gabrieli Ensemble performed in 1976. Joan and Hestor Dickson came to the Club in 1977. Victoria De Los Angeles visited in 1982. In 1983 came the Songmakers Almanac. This last named group was composed of Graham Johnson, Richard Jackson and Sally Burgess. They performed recitals under the title of 'Our pleasant vices'. Graham Johnson has recently been awarded an OBE and is currently undertaking the colossal task of recording every known Schubert song, of which there are over six hundred. They will be available on Hyperion CD's. Fischer Deskau was another distinguished visitor to the Club.

It is well known that the demise of the Music Club took place after it moved to the MacRobert Centre. Chamber music is today a minority interest, very rarely promoted in the smaller centres. There are rarely any solo recitals or chamber music (although during 1994/1995 the MacRobert will host two chamber music groups). The taste in music in this area has shifted as a result. The Music Chief said to me in 1956 'you are going to the worst musical desert in Scotland'. As far as music in schools is concerned, that desert was certainly not in Bridge of Allan. Everybody who was anybody came to the Bridge of Allan Music Club and many people were very upset to hear it had disbanded. It was a national institution. Thank you".

Mr McVicar was duly applauded and thanked for his lecture. Conversation then began, with much regret being expressed for the demise of the Music Club.

Demise of the Music Club, and of the Museum Hall

One reason for the Club's demise was financial difficulties. Artists fees were rising and it was becoming increasingly difficult to support these through subscriptions. It is generally conceded, however, as George McVicar pointed out, that the biggest mistake made was to move to the MacRobert.The entire history of the Music Club and the earlier Public Interests Association belonged to the Museum Hall. In a critique by Bill Kitching in October 1971 (the year the Club moved to the MacRobert), whilst he appreciated the advantages of the MacRobert, he premeditated the fate of the Music Club; "It might be said that the Bridge of Allan and District Music Club, which succeeded the Public Interests Association in promoting concerts of the highest order since the 1920's, has lost its identity in deserting the Museum Hall for the MacRobert Centre. There is certainly no mention of it in the inaugural programme. But it does not seem to have lost its supporters; and its gains can be measured in terms of the University Steinway, and a rather more comfortable and intimate hall. It also seemed right that the Club should be putting on the very first recital in the main auditorium on Monday night. The facilities for refreshments must also be commended".

It is easy to see why the Music Club moved. The Museum Hall by 1971 was old-fashioned and in a bad state of repair, through lack of attention by its owners, the Burgh Council. At the time most local authorities merely tolerated public halls. In 1950, Dr Welsh (who along with some others had bought the hall in 1939 and ran it as a private company) passed ownership and running of the hall, on behalf of the common good, to the Burgh Council. Facilities for the artist and patron in the hall were at a bare minimum and modern standards of comfort were non-existent. The MacRobert, opened in 1971, on the other hand was modern, clean, comfortable and had professional standard equipment and facilities.

Yet, despite its shortcomings, the atmosphere which existed in the Museum Hall had transcended the problems and left an indelible impression on people's minds. It was an atmosphere which the MacRobert could not capture. Dr Welsh later wrote "The audience said there was an intimacy and friendliness about the Museum Hall which is lacking in the MacRobert theatre at the University". The geographical position of the Museum Hall was also more favourable to a large number of the Club's supporters who were elderly. Many were not in a position to make the more lengthy journey to the MacRobert and back to the village afterwards.

The most important factor of the Museum Hall from both the performer and the patron's point of view was, and still is, its perfect natural acoustics – it being the only venue in the area to have such an essential and priceless advantage. The combination of intimate atmosphere and fine acoustics meant the Museum Hall and the Music Club fitted hand and glove together. Indeed with better management, the Hall might never have lost such a valuable friend. A hard lesson to learn has been that music and community spirit in the Bridge of Allan area, as well as farther afield, has paid dearly for the closure of the

Museum Hall, as it has with the disbandonment of the Music Club.

The Museum Hall today

In 1979, when the Music Club was still in existence, the campaign to protect the Museum Hall for future generations began. The future of the hall was in doubt, as it had been in 1939 when Dr Welsh bought it over. That year (1979) the hall was closed by Stirling District Council – inheritors of the Burgh Council's duties and assets. It said the hall was surplus to requirements and was structurally unsound. Immediately, campaign foundations were laid by, appropriately, the Dr Welsh Educational and Historical Trust, who stopped the hall from being demolished in 1983, the Scottish Civic Trust and Bridge of Allan Community Council. In 1987 the Museum Hall Association (MHA) was set up by Mr David Wilson to push for the retention and restoration of the hall. First secretary was the late David Angus who, being on the Dr Welsh Trust had helped save the hall in 1983 and had also been a key factor in the saving and restoration of Callendar House in Falkirk. The Association was set up on the basis of "a petition bearing one thousand five hundred signatures. Over fifty local companies gave their written support, urging restoration of the Museum Hall". Over the years, there have been five petitions, from local citizens, teenagers, school children and farmers.

The campaign, which is still on-going, has received support from the National Trust for Scotland, who said of this 'notable building' that "while some repair work has been carried out on the external roof structure to make it at least wind and watertight; this can only be a first step in a comprehensive repair and restoration programme for the whole building ... it is clear that there is a wide body of support within the local community for the restoration of the Hall ... that it may in future be of benefit to all sections of the community, and a building which your Council can be proud to be associated with". Support has also come from; Scottish Civic Trust, Scottish Architectural Heritage, Stirling Civic Trust, The Lord Lieutenant of Stirling and Falkirk, distinguished personalities, Central Regional Council, Stirling University, Stirling Management Centre, Stirling University Sports Centre, who said "the potential of the Museum Hall is obvious; the increasing size of the university population will require additional hall accomodation, and this in turn will reduce the facilities available to non-university groups. The presence of a suitable hall adjacent to the campus would offer the necessary additional accomodation, both for the University and for the community".

David Wilson, who is still chairing the Association, has said "The Museum Hall Association proposals conform with the legacy of Dr Welsh and his co-directors who, having sought the guarantee of law on the presumption that the council of the day and their successors would have the integrity to honour legal agreement encompassed by the deed of transfer, transferred the ownership of the hall to the local authority back in 1950. The agreement sought and won by these fine people was that the hall would be maintained for all time for the benefit of the people of Bridge of Allan. MHA proposals are many faceted – community use, concert hall, amateur Arts centre, use by organisations such as the MacRobert Centre for rehearsal facility and venue and a role in education and tourism. The Association agrees wholeheartedly with Roy McEwen when, as Director of the MacRobert, he said 'there are a number of things that go on at the MacRobert that would be better suited to a Victorian concert hall'.

There is no conflict between the Museum Hall Association proposals and the MacRobert Centre or its management. Indeed not only do the proposals complement the work of the MacRobert, they include proposals that would be to the benefit of the Albert Hall and Smith Gallery as well. Policy that generates conflict is bad policy, our policy advocates co-operation and a unified approach to marketing the whole area as a destination where a variety of venues provide a wholesome variety of entertainment and interest. No one thing can be everything – the Museum Hall has its unquestionable merits and demerits and this is the case also with the MacRobert and the Albert Halls. Each is an important part of the complete picture, each as if parts in a jigsaw interlocking and joining together.

If an explanation as to the merits of excellent acoustics to certain categories of artists, by those who dictate Arts policy and provision is necessary, then questions should be asked of them and not the Museum Hall Association. It is simply a matter of cold, hard fact that the Museum Hall is the best acoustic venue in the District and as such is a major asset to those charged with promoting the Arts to the best standard possible. The notion that the MacRobert staff only have a professional standard and ability within their own building is of course, nonsense. There is no question that such ability cannot be transported the short distance to the Museum Hall and used to best advantage in promoting concerts or whatever on those occasions it is deemed appropriate, leaving the rest of the year to community events, tourism and of course the amateur Arts. Versatility creates viablility".

George McVicar, in a letter of support to the Museum Hall Association, wished to "draw attention to the change in the type of musical concert now available in this area, a change for which the closure of the Museum Hall is in the main responsible … It may well be argued that public taste has changed, but, in my view, the disappearance of the solo or chamber music recital is due to the lack of a hall with appropriate ambience and the right acoustics. These were exactly the qualities possessed by the Museum Hall and its closure has been and probably will go on, depriving the district of the most intimate and, in the end, the most satisfying type of musical concert". He described the hall as having "the correct intimacy of atmosphere" and "admirable acoustic quality".

Kenneth Richardson, Arts Director of the Barbican Centre remembered the Museum Hall with considerable affection – "The Museum Hall was an important part of my early musical education. I well remember Music Club concerts there as well as other events (Any Questions among them). It is a great sadness to me when I come back to Bridge of Allan from time to time to see the disrepair into which the Hall has fallen in recent times".

Alexander Oliver also feels the Museum Hall still has a part to play in the life of Bridge of Allan, "The Museum Hall forms a major part of my very earliest memories of Bridge of Allan. I can still clearly recall the sense of awe I felt as a very small child when I was taken there by my mother for my earliest exposure to live music and performance. I can also remember very clearly the sense of pride and achievement when I first 'made it' on to the stage there – first as a diminutive (and probably nauseating!) puppeteer, then as a quite spectacularly untalented violinist and finally, before leaving Scotland to further my studies in Vienna, as an emergent singer. Powerful stuff as part of anyone's tapestry of early memories, so it is hardly surprising that it is with a sense of real shock and outrage that I learn that the Hall is now under threat of demolition. I simply cannot believe that the Museum Hall has no longer any useful function to perform in the artistic and social life of Bridge of Allan and feel in the strongest possible terms that its demolition would be an act of mindless vandalism which cannot and must not be tolerated by anyone who cares about the aesthetic and historical value of Bridge of Allan."

Lord Younger (ex-secretary of state for Scotland) is also keen to see the Museum Hall restored "I am very sad that it has got into such a bad state. I have often enjoyed concerts there in the past when it was undoubtedly a very fine concert hall ... I frequently made use of it during my time as secretary and chairman of the Stirling and District Choral Union. We regularly gave concerts there, with great success. I feel sure that a concert hall of this quality is very necessary in a major town with a University, such as Stirling."

Both Secretaries of State for Scotland Malcolm Rifkind and Ian Lang, James Douglas Hamilton and Michael Forsyth MP have all made statements confirming the substantial and unlawful neglect of the Museum Hall by Stirling District Council, ironically a member of the Stirling Initiative which is spending £100m on, among other things, restoring buildings within the Stirling town area. None of these has been the subject of any public initiated campaign or representations as has been the Museum Hall. The support of numerous prestigious organisations, some already mentioned, could be realised financially by a wide variety of funding sources, some eligible and already promised, and now possibly added to by the National Lottery through the National Heritage Fund.

When the subsidence problem has been cured and repairs and restorations have been achieved there must be competent management with high standards in facilities and user and visitor comfort. The lack of attention to these in the past has been a prime cause of the deterioration and loss of the Hall. The fifteen year old campaign continues and it is perfectly clear that the Hall is wanted and needed by the community, and now it has the assistance of the Friends of the Museum Hall.

The future is currently undecided for the most protected building in Bridge of Allan which Ella MacLean in her book *Bridge of Allan – the rise of a village* said, "Bridge of Allan was particularly fortunate in having". As the Bridge of Allan and District Music Club lost its identity by moving away from the Museum Hall, it is quite possible that Bridge of Allan too will lose its identity, if it loses the Museum Hall.

Old Music Hall – wooden building with rustic tree trunk pillars – demolished 1902.

Museum Hall 1923.

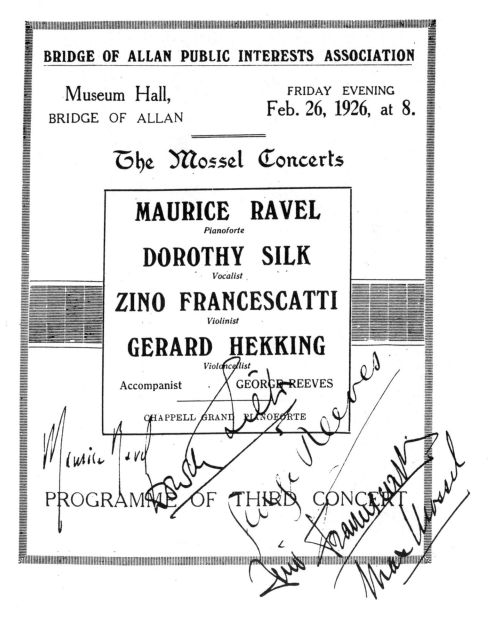

BRIDGE OF ALLAN PUBLIC INTERESTS ASSOCIATION

Museum Hall,
BRIDGE OF ALLAN

FRIDAY EVENING
Feb. 26, 1926, at 8.

The Mossel Concerts

MAURICE RAVEL
Pianoforte

DOROTHY SILK
Vocalist

ZINO FRANCESCATTI
Violinist

GERARD HEKKING
Violoncellist

Accompanist · GEORGE REEVES

CHAPPELL GRAND PIANOFORTE

PROGRAMME OF THIRD CONCERT

Public Interests Association Mossel Concerts 1926.

Dennis Noble – baritone   Suggia – world renowned cellist

Harold Bauer – leading pianist

Maggie Teyte – famed soprano

Some of the celebrities of the PIA Concerts 1927-28.

CONCERTS.

FIRST CONCERT.—Thursday, 11th October.

Piano Recital.

LOUIS KENTNER.

SECOND CONCERT.—Friday, 7th December,

Two Pianos—Recital.

CYRIL SMITH and PHYLLIS SELLICK.

THIRD CONCERT.—Thursday, 17th January.

Vocal and Instrumental Recital.

ROY HENDERSON, AILIE CULLEN, JOHN McARTHUR.

FOURTH CONCERT.—Wednesday, 13th February.

ZORIAN STRING QUARTET.

Chairman of Committee:

Mrs. IRWIN, Westerton, Bridge of Allan.

Hon. Secretary:

Miss D. B. WILSON, Ardmhor, Bridge of Allan.

BRIDGE OF ALLAN and DISTRICT MUSIC CLUB.

This Club has been formed in association with the Arts Council of Great Britain (late C.E.M.A.) to provide yearly a winter season of first-class Concerts.

For the present (1945-46) programme, detailed on next page, the arrangements have been carried through by Mrs. Lindsay Forster, Dullanbrae, Bridge of Allan, Chairman till lately and now Vice-President of the Glasgow Chamber Music Society.

The Club is making a tentative beginning, and is not yet venturing on all the activities that have been suggested for it. Later, it is hoped to have something more to offer to its supporters on the basis of a membership subscription. The Club offers the following programme for its first season, with ordinary tickets at 7/6 and 4/- per Concert, and with a Season Ticket for the former class of seats at 25/- for the four Concerts. Guarantees have also been obtained (promises) and more are wanted. Guarantors are asked to state an amount (£1 to £5).

Application for Season Tickets must be made (with remittance) to the Hon. Secretary.

The Single Tickets will be on sale at the following shops:—

Hay, Stirling.
Cadien, Bridge of Allan.
Jackson, Bridge of Allan.
Hutchison, Dunblane.

It is hoped to arrange for bus services to be suitably supplemented between Bridge of Allan and places round about on Concert nights.

Launch of the Music Club, and its first concerts 1945-46.

First Concert—

WEDNESDAY, 20th OCTOBER, 1948

Violin and Piano Recital

CAMPOLI

AND

ERIC GRITTON

✤

Second Concert—

WEDNESDAY, 17th NOVEMBER, 1948

Two Pianos Recital

WIGHT HENDERSON

AND

HERRICK BUNNEY

✤

Third Concert—

THURSDAY, 16th December, 1948

Piano Recital

DENIS MATTHEWS

Fourth Concert—

TUESDAY, 18th JANUARY, 1949

THE LONDON BELGIAN PIANOFORTE QUARTET

✤

Fifth Concert—

SATURDAY, 12th FEBRUARY, 1949.

Vocal and Piano Recital

PETER PEARS

AND

BENJAMIN BRITTEN

✤

All these Concerts will be given

in the

MUSEUM HALL

BRIDGE OF ALLAN

At 8 p.m.

Music Club programme 1948-49.

BLAIRLOGIE:
A Short History of Central Scotland's
First Conservation Village

Alastair Maxwell-Irving

To step into the old village of Blairlogie is to take a step back in time, – apart, sadly, from the seemingly inevitable cars and electricity poles. It has been described as one of the loveliest villages in Scotland, and, because of its unique character and charm, was chosen to feature in the original television series of Dr Finlay's Casebook. Nestling under the steep southern escarpment of the Ochil hills, with Dumyat rising steeply 1373 feet above it, and dominated by its 16th century castle, Blairlogie is still essentially an 18th century village. It is the first of the towns and villages stretching east for some thirteen miles from Stirling to Dollar that constitute 'The Hillfoots', the dramatic natural boundary between the precipitous Ochils to the north and the flat carse-lands of the meandering Forth valley to the south; and ever since the present main road, the 'new turnpike road', was built in 1806, the older parts of these communities have been effectively by-passed, and thus largely spared from the uglier excesses of modern development.

The earliest record of Blairlogie is in 1451, when King James II gave the lands to his queen, Mary of Gueldres, as part of her dowry. Half a century later, King James IV granted the lands in feu to James Spittal, a prosperous Stirling merchant and bailie in the town, though his family had first acquired possession of 'Blair of Logy' several decades earlier. The Spittals were prominent in the life of Stirling in the 16th century, as well as serving successive kings and queens at court. It was Alexander Spittal who, in 1543, built the original tower-house at Blairlogie now known as 'The Blair' on an outcrop of rock beside the Burn of Blair. It is a small, rectangular building, three storeys in height, with two vaulted chambers in the basement, a corbelled-out stair turret at the SE corner and another, defensive turret at the SW corner. The second floor was partly contained within the roof, and is provided with early examples of dormer windows, which bear the date of construction. Originally, there was no connection between the basement and the hall on the first floor, each having its own external entrance. The tower was enlarged by Alexander's grandson, Adam, who added the east wing in 1582; and the castle has been further extended and altered during subsequent centuries.

The Spittals and their descendants continued as lairds of Blairlogie until 1845, when the estate was purchased by Robert Bruce of Kennet. He had served in the Grenadier Guards at the battle of Waterloo and was later member of parliament for Clackmannanshire. His son, Alexander Bruce, succeeded as 6th Lord Balfour of Burleigh in 1869. Seven years later he was elected a representative peer for Scotland, an office he held for the next 45 years. Meanwhile, in 1891, he sold the estate of Blairlogie to Lieutenant Colonel James

Hare of Calder Hall, who had for many years been commissioner for the Earl of Hopetoun. On the death of Colonel Hare in 1928, Blairlogie passed to his only son, Major General Sir Steuart Hare; but Sir Steuart chose to live elsewhere, and in 1951 he gave the estate to his eldest son, Major General James, later Sir James, Hare. It was Sir James who finally broke up the estate and sold it off.

A community would quickly have grown up on the land beneath the castle where the old 'King's Highway' passed, but it was not until the middle of the 18th century that the present village became established, when it achieved fame in its own right as a goat's milk resort. A large herd of goats was kept on the hillside behind the village square, and invalids came from far and wide to drink the beneficial milk. *The New Statistical Account of Scotland*, published in 1842, remarks that Blairlogie had "long been a favourite resort for invalids in spring and summer". "At the Goats' Milk at Blair" is said to have been a common expression. But soon afterwards Blairlogie was eclipsed in popularity by the new mineral springs at nearby Airthrey and the Hydropathic Hotel (1864) and numerous lodging houses being built in the adjacent new town of Bridge of Allan in the same parish.

The majority of the houses in Blairlogie date from this early period. Montana Cottage on the north side of the square, although largely remodelled, and Blair House to the SE both bear the date 1765, while Croft House at the SW corner of the square, the largest house in the village, and Blairlogie Cottage, another fine 2-storeyed house at the west end of the village, are not much later. The old manse also dated from c1765.

In those days the main road ran right through the square – as did the burn, and it was along this road on either side that single storey and 2-storey cottages quickly sprang up. Some of the simpler cottages had clay mortar walls and thatched roofs, while others had the more expensive pantiles and crow-stepped gables, but all were harled on the outside and no doubt coated with the traditional white lime-wash. Another group of cottages ran south along the burn and then turned up a lane to the west. One of the last of these cottages, a group of three single storey buildings with clay mortar walls and thatched roofs, bore the date 1758; but although they were occupied within living memory, only the foundations and date-stone now remain.

Three of the cottages along the old highway, which included one of two storeys with an outside stair to the upper floor, now comprise the village hall. The most easterly of these was originally given to the village c1900 by Colonel Hare as the village 'Reading Room', the alternative name by which the hall is still known. It had served as a village library for as long as anyone could remember, and may have been the same building as the public library that is known to have existed in the village as early as the 18th century. The rest of the hall, including the 2-storeyed Crowsteps Cottage, was purchased by the Reading Room Committee in 1947 (for £55). The latter cottage incorporates an 18th century sundial just below the eaves, but sadly its windows have been 'modernised.'

At the same time as Blairlogie was establishing itself as a health resort, the religious life of the parish of Logie was in turmoil over the vexed question of the right of heritors to appoint a minister against the wishes of the congregation. It became a dispute of national importance. Matters finally came to a head in 1761, when the entire Kirk Session at Logie 'seceded', and formed themselves into a separate religious body. This became the Relief Congregation at Blairlogie. The following year, with the help of the newly formed Presbytery of Relief, Blairlogie obtained the first minister of its own choice, and in 1765 built a new church on the south side of the village. A manse was also built about the same time. The church was accidentally burned down in 1845, but it was rebuilt within the old walls a year later and is still in use. It is now part of the United Free Church.

The rise of Bridge of Allan as a 'spa' in the 19th century, and the renewed prominence of the alternative road north to Perth through Dunblane, Blackford and Auchterarder, put an end to Blairlogie as a popular resort and stopping place, while the little traffic that did continue to travel along the Hillfoots now by-passed the village on the new road. Blairlogie had become caught in time. While fine new houses went up a pace in Stirling, Bridge of Allan and elsewhere in the neighbourhood, Blairlogie scarcely changed. The sole exceptions were the manse, on the southern edge of the village, which was rebuilt in 1865, and Telford House, a small classical dwelling that was built slightly later to the same design as nearby Blairlogie Park. Contrary to popular belief the name has no connection with Thomas Telford, the famous civil engineer and architect, but commemorates the Telford family of masons, and later bankers, who lived in the village for many generations. Their earlier home, which was built in 1728 on 'John Telford's Feu', was demolished to make way for the new house. William Telford was one of the seven partners who founded the first private bank in Stirling in 1777.

During the 20th century, some of the old buildings, including at least four cottages and a smithy, became so ruinous that they were demolished, and scarcely a trace now remains, although they are still remembered. Others, such as Montana Cottage, Croft Cottage and Hillside Cottage, have been remodelled and restored. Only one building, Ivydean, which was originally two cottages, has been so modernised as to completely disguise any original features that remain, while, with one exception, all the new houses to be built are along the present main road, the new turnpike road of 1806. This road has seen a dramatic increase in traffic this century, from the Dollar mail bus, the daily open horse-brake and an occasional car during the early years of the century, to the present seemingly endless convoys of vehicles on what is now a major trunk road between Stirling and the east.

Since the Second World War the village has seen a resurgence of life, this time as an artistic centre. Not only do several notable artists live in the village itself, but the popular Crowsteps' art exhibition, which was held annually from 1966 until 1982, and more recent exhibitions by artists of both local and national importance have all been hugely successful. The gardens have also been open to the public under Scotland's Gardens Scheme, as well as for the benefit of other local charities.

But the credit for establishing Blairlogie as the first Conservation Village in Central Scotland, and only the second in the country as a whole, is largely due to the enthusiasm and perseverance of the late Moultrie Kelsall, the distinguished writer, actor and producer, who came to live in the village in 1940. At a time when much of the village was run down and parts falling into ruin, he purchased a row of condemned cottages, restored two of them as his own home, Kirklea Cottage, helped restore the fabric of the church, and took a personal interest in the rejuvenation of the rest of the village. He was then instrumental in getting Blairlogie made the first village in the region to be designated a 'Conservation Area' under the Civic Amenities Act of 1967. It was a cause dear to his heart, and one which he espoused in the book *A Future for the Past*, of which he was coauthor with the architect Stuart Harris, and which he dedicated to "reversing the monumental wastage of old buildings."

References and sources

150 Years in Blairlogie: the Story of Blairlogie Church, by Rev. R. F. Anderson. 1912.
Blairlogie – About Sixty Years Ago, by D. M. Anderson. 1967.
Logie: A Parish History, by R. M. Fergusson. 1905. 2 volumes.
Minutes of Blairlogie Reading Room and Blairlogie Ratepayers' Association.
Stirling Journal.
Registrum Magni Sigilli.
Scottish Record Office.
Burke's Landed Gentry.

'The Blair', Blairlogie Castle – 1543 tower-house in foreground, oriel window added in 1890's.

Former King's Highway – village hall on right.

The 18thC Square – Ivy Cottage on left and Montana Cottage.

Croft House on left with Square beyond.

Hillside Cottage with village hall beyond.

THE TRIAL OF FRANCIS BUCHANAN 1746

George Thomson

The following transcription (in italics) is of an extract from the *Court Book* of Carlisle in the Cumbria Archives. It was noted in the course of research for material of interest to the forthcoming 250th anniversary of the Jacobite Rebellion.

Sept 27 1746

Francis Buchanan

called – Arn Prior

John Finlayson – proves a Letter

Archibald Anderson – of Allan [presumably Bridge of Allan]

Robert Cadle – saw them near Down – running toward Dunblain –

Duncan McNaughton – saw him in Stirlingshire –

Donald Ferguson – his servant and serjeant

X George Drummond & many other Witnesses who gave him the Character of a friend to the Government & that he had allways express'd his Detestation of the Rebellion &c.

But the Case was plainly prov'd & the Jury found him guilty

tried by Lord Chief Baron, he is a Laird of good Estate – & is called Arne Prior – his trial last 8. hours & all the 4. Judges present.

PEOPLE OF THE FORTH (3) Part 2
DAVID BRUCE - medical scientist, soldier, naturalist.

G. F. Follett

A previous article (Mitchell 1989) in this series on the People of the Forth covered the early years of Stirling's adopted son David Bruce – family home Victoria Square, school Stirling High. At university he began his studies in zoology, but changed and graduated Bachelor of Medicine and Master of Surgery at Edinburgh in 1881. His life long love was natural history and remarkable as was his work in medicine it was approached from the biological and natural history point of view. His unusual insight and skills were powered by his natural history drive (B.J.R. 1932).

He began his medical career at a time when understanding of the causes of infectious diseases was increasing rapidly and in later years he recalled an incident that may have played a part in determining the direction of his life's work.

"I can well remember the day in 1882 when I met a fellow student who had just returned to Edinburgh from Germany. He told me that it had been recently discovered (by Robert Koch) that the disease (tuberculosis) was really caused by a living germ the tubercle bacillus. It was difficult at first to believe such a radicle idea..."

But first he was to spend a short period in general practice as assistant to Dr Stone in Reigate, Surrey and in 1883 he married Mary Elizabeth Steele, the daughter of Dr Stone's predecessor in the practice. As his wife and fellow-worker in all his scientific work, Mary was to have a profound influence on his life and career. General practice was however not to Bruce's liking. He soon joined the Army Medical service, was commissioned Surgeon Captain in August 1883, and in the following year was posted to Malta.

MALTA FEVER – THE CAUSE

As Resident Medical Officer at Station Hospital, Valletta Bruce was initially at least not too busy, finding time to dredge in the surrounding seas for marine creatures and discussing their identification Here Mary's scale drawings were invaluable in correspondence with specialists to whom he sent specimens. In one tube of copepeda (microscopic life in plankton) which Bruce sent him, I. C. Thompson found a previously unknown specimen which he named *Copilia Brucii*.

When Bruce began his work on Malta fever it was a major health problem among army and navy personnel stationed on the island. In 1887 there were 104 cases amongst 2200 troops, four men died and nine were invalided home. His investigations began with a study of the incidence over the preceding eleven years of typhoid and malta fever which at that time were not clearly differentiated from each other. Malta fever he found peaked in May to July and typhoid in September to November but there was no correlation with temperature or rainfall. He next studied the clinical features of some 91 cases seen during 1886. A number of treatments were tried and judged to be equally ineffective. One he did not try was the subcutaneous injection of quinine which one officer claimed had cured him but Bruce "did not see justification to try the method on private soldiers in the hospital" since the officer advocating it as a treatment complained of intractable ulcers at the injection sites.

On Boxing day 1886 a young soldier died in the 15th day of his illness. At post-mortem Bruce found in the spleen "single micrococci in enormous numbers scattered throughout the section". This he compared with the spleen in typhoid fever where large clumps of bacteria are found. Bruce then sought the help of the government analyst Dr Carrusa Scilure in preparing sterile agar jelly on which he cultured finger tip blood from 10 severe cases of fever. Of some 30 to 40 attempts only two cultures did not remain sterile and as the organisms grown in each case were different they were considered to be contaminants. (At that time vein puncture was rarely used to collect blood. Nowadays using a syringe to take a relatively large amount of blood and with improved culture techniques in the laboratory it is usually possible to grow the organism from blood).

Contamination was likely to be a much greater problem when cultures were made in the post-mortem room so at the autopsy on the next fatal case Bruce removed the spleen wrapped it in a cloth soaked in disinfectant and took it to a small quiet room in his quarters. There with the windows shut to avoid drafts and using antiseptic techniques he opened the spleen and made cultures from the splenic pulp. From this culture and samples from several other fatal cases he grew an organism which he called *Micrococcus Melitensis*. In 1920 the organism was placed in a separate genus and named in Bruce's honour, *Brucella*.

Using the same technique from the spleens of three fatal cases of typhoid fever he grew the bacillus recognised as the cause of that disease (Salmonella typhi). In reporting the cultural characteristics of this organism Bruce admitted a lack of experience in this new science of bacteriology, and getting leave in 1888 he and Mary went at their own expense to Koch's laboratory in Berlin and studied the latest techniques of bacterial culture, staining and microscopy. Returning to military service in 1889 he was appointed Assistant Professor of Pathology at the Royal Army Medical College at Netley and there started a course in bacteriology, said to be the first at any medical school in the United Kingdom.

TETSE FLY DISEASE

In 1894 Bruce was posted to Pietermaritzburg in Natal, South Africa. The then Governor of Natal and High Commissioner for Zululand was Sir Walter Hely-Hutchinson who had been Lieutenant Governor of Malta when Bruce was working on Malta fever. He asked Bruce soon after his arrival to investigate 'Nagana' a disease affecting the cattle of natives in the north of Zululand. The Bruces left Pietermaritzburg on the 27th October 1894 but it took five weeks of travel by mule or oxwagon to reach Ubombo where a small mud hut had been provided for their use. Ubombo is 600m (2000ft) above sea level in the Lebomba hills and separated by a coastal plain from the sea 60 miles away. On the plain are several Tetse Fly areas. Bacterial examination of the blood and organs of affected cattle brought in by natives was not helpful. In Bruce's stained blood films occasional objects were seen but thought to be artefacts. In wet blood films occasional active parasites seen were thought by Bruce to be Filaria (worms). It was not until he returned to Natal and could consult textbooks that he realised they were trypanosomes (flagelate protozoa). The parasites were scarce in cattle but if blood from affected animals was injected into horses or dogs the organisms were found in abundance in the blood of those species.

In January 1895 Bruce was recalled by the army to Pietermaritzburg. The only transport available was a donkey cart for their luggage. The Bruces had to walk. At one point the donkeys nearly died of thirst. Eventually they met an ox wagon sent for them but the journey continued to be difficult because the oxen were untrained. In Pietermaritzburg they found no reason for their recall. Was it, as Bruce seemed to think, because the army authorities had not been consulted about his research? At any rate it took Sir Hely-Hutchinson nearly a year to get, from the Secretary of State in London, permission for Bruce to return to his work on the Nagana disease. The journey back to Ubombo was easier, they travelled on horseback and it only took a week.

During the next two years working alone, isolated, in primitive conditions they did what is generally considered to be Bruce's best work. There were two theories about the cause of Nagana. One recognised the association with Tetse Fly but thought that when biting it must inject a toxin. The other theory, held by the local people, related it to wild game and believed the disease to be transmitted by saliva or excreta on the grass eaten by cattle.

To test the first theory healthy oxen and dogs were sent from the hills down to the Tetse Fly belt on the coastal plain. When returned to Ubombo they were found to be infected. Tetse Fly caught in gauze cages were brought from the fly belt to Ubombo and allowed to feed on healthy cattle who then became infected. The blood of wild game animals was examined for trypanosomes but none found. Knowing how difficult it can be to find trypanosomes in the blood of cattle as compared with horses or dogs, Bruce injected the blood from ten different game animals which he had shot, into dogs who soon sickened and died of the disease.

To test the second theory horses were muzzled and driven down to 'fly country' during the day and returned to the hills where they were fed at night. They developed the disease. Animals kept in the hills and fed foliage brought from the fly infected areas did not develop the disease. Bruce concluded that Nagana was transmitted by Tetse flies and wild game were a reservoir of the disease.

In 1897 Bruce was looking more closely at the Tetse Fly and found trypanosomes in the gut for up to five days after biting an infected animal. Unfortunately he then stopped the study. Had he continued for another two weeks he might have predated by 12 years Kleine's discovery of the cyclical life history of the trypanosome

THE BOER WAR

Returning to military duties Bruce saw his first battle on 21st October 1899 at Elandslaagte station and operated continuously for 30 hours. Despite their success at Elandslaagte the British were surrounded and withdrew to Ladysmith where they remained besieged until 27th February 1900. At first Bruce was in charge of the military hospital in the protestant church and later the large hospital at Intombe camp where he had a staff of one RAMC Officer, seven civilian doctors and 17 nursing sisters. There were about 1000 patients mostly with typhoid fever or dysentery. Several of the civilian doctors were sick the whole time and Bruce himself succumbed to typhoid fever for the last four weeks of the siege.

Mary 'made herself useful' running a library, looking after the medical officers mess, helping in the operating tent, taking notes and helping the sisters. 'Looking after the mess' included "disguising the fact from some people – who thought they could not eat horse which she thought 'very good food – much nicer than the old trek ox".

After the siege Bruce was given a months leave. He was convalescing from typhoid and Mary's weight was down to seven stone eleven pounds. They spent the time staying at local farms, resting, enjoying fresh food, and riding together although most of the good horses, including Mary's pet horse, had been taken by the Boers. Returning to active duty Bruce saw further action at Laings Nek and Belfast. They returned to the United Kingdom in October 1901.

SLEEPING SICKNESS

From 1899-1905 sleeping sickness previously unknown in Uganda killed 250,000 people. It was thought that the disease may have spread from West Africa where it had been known for years. Bruce thought that Emin Pasha's men may have brought it from the Congo. Not knowing the cause or mode of spread of the disease the British Government feared that it could spread down the Nile to Suez and thence possibly to India.

The Royal Society was asked to appoint a commission to investigate the disease and their team of George C Low, Aldo Castellani and C Christy arrived at Kisun in July 1902. Individually each was a capable scientist but they could not work together as a team and Christy left after three months and Low before the end of the year. Before he left Low as leader of the commission wrote to Sir Patrick Manson on 15th October 1902 informing him that Castellani had found a "fish like parasite darting about" in the cerebro-spinal fluid (CSF) of some cases of the disease. Nevertheless he expressed the view that a streptococcus or similar organism caused the disease, a view apparently shared by Castellani at the time.

In February 1903 Bruce was seconded by the War Office to take charge of the commission and he arrived at Entebbe on 16th March with Mary, two RAMC Officers and an NCO. Castellani showed Bruce the parasite he had found in the CSF of five cases and in the blood of one. In the three weeks before Castellani left, the newcomers helped him examine the CSF of 29 patients in twenty of whom trypanosomes were found while the CSF of 13 control patient were negative.

Subsequently the events of these few weeks gave rise to a long dispute in the medical press and the Times. Castellani was obsessed with the question of priority and felt that he was not given the credit he deserved for this discovery of the Trypanosome causing sleeping sickness. Bruce agreed that the parasite had been seen first by Castellani and acknowledged that Castellani's method of centrifuging the CSF before examination (first used in his work on the streptococcus) had been instrumental in their successful identification of the parasite in so many cases of the disease. On the other hand Castellani had not at first appreciated the signification of his observation and had done little work in the four to five months between his first observation of the parasite and Bruce's arrival at Entebbe. The Bruces returned to Britain in August 1903.

MALTA FEVER - CONTINUED

Identifying the organism causing Malta fever had not lead to any understanding of the way the disease spread and it remained a major health problem among soldiers and sailors stationed in Malta. In 1904 Bruce was made chairman of a commission sent to Malta to investigate how the disease was transmitted.

In their first year of work they re-examined the incidence of the disease and noted that it was more than three times as common in officers and their families as in other ranks. Furthermore among the local population it was more common in country districts than in Valletta. They injected goats with cultures of the organism Bruce had discovered and called *Micrococcus Mellitensis* but the goats appeared unaffected.

The next year Dr Zammit a Maltese member of the commission who had kept one or two of the inoculated goats tested their blood serum and found that it agglutinated cultures of the micrococcus causing Malta fever. It was soon shown that although apparently healthy 50% of goats on the island were infected and 10% were excreting the organism in their milk. Monkeys fed with milk from affected goats for just one day, developed the disease. As soon as the consumption of goats milk by British service personnel and their families was forbidden, Malta fever ceased to be a problem.

Although an obviously correct decision from the point of view of the army medical services, it destroyed overnight the livelihood of many goat-keepers on the island. Naturally they protested the innocence of their goats, even going on strike for a few days, and the debate about the role of the Maltese goat in the spread of Malta fever continued for several years. It was to be another 50 years before pasteurisation of goats milk became compulsory on the island and the disease ceased to be common in the civilian population.

Bruce was by now an eminent medical scientist and was to lead teams working on sleeping sickness and its vectors in Uganda from 1908 to 1910 and in Nyasaland from 1911 to 1913. But his involvement with Malta fever was not quite finished. In 1908 while passing through Kampala on his way to the Sleeping Sickness Commission's centre at Mpumu, he was told of a new outbreak of a fever 'Mulingo' in the province of Ankola. Three doctors using only clinical methods of investigation had already suggested three different diagnoses. Bruce went to Ankola where he saw some 40 cases. In a series of experiments which were elegant in their simplicity, using bacterial cultures and blood samples sent from Malta as well as those obtained in Ankola, he showed that Mulingo was in fact Malta fever, identical in everyway, including spreading by goats.

Throughout their busy years in Africa the Bruces maintained an interest in Natural History. From Ubombo in 1898 Mary sent a collection of butterflies to the Durban Museum and during the first decade of this century Bruce sent collections of insects and skins and skulls of larger animals to the Natural History Museum in London.

THE GREAT WAR

From 1914 to 1919 Bruce was Commander of the Royal Army Medical College. He was chairman of the War Office Committee on Tetanus which proved the value of anti-tetanus serum in preventing tetanus in the wounded. He also chaired the Trench-fever Committee. In 1919 he went on the retired list as Major-General. He was the recipient of many academic honours including Fellowship of the Royal Society (1899), and Knighthood (1918).

Mary died at their home in London on 23rd November 1931. Bruce was by that time seriously ill and when an obituary of her was read to him, he said "Should any notice appear about myself, you might see that my wife gets full credit for all the work she has done to assist me". Never apart, she worked with him everywhere and just four days later during her funeral service, he died. He was cremated at Golders Green Crematorium and his ashes interned in the family plot in the graveyard of the Church of the Holy Rude at Stirling.

REFERENCES AND FURTHER READING

B.R.J. 1932 Sir David Bruce. Obituary Notices of Fellows of the Royal Society. No. 1 pp79-85.

BOYD, J. 1973. The Castellani-Bruce Controversy. *Notes and records of the Royal Society of London* 28, 93-110

BRUCE, D. 1887. Notes on the discovery of a micro-organism in Malta fever. *Practitioner* 39, 161 - 170.

BRUCE, D. 1888. The Micrococcus of Malta fever. Ibid 40, 241 - 249.

BRUCE, D. and the EARL OF CROMER. 1910. The advancement of medicine by research. *Lancet* 1, 1635 - 1638.

BRUCE, D 1915. Croonian lecture II - Glossina Morsitans : Trypanosoma Brucei : wild game, and lecture III - Trypanosoma Gambiense and Congo sleeping sickness. *British Medical Journal* 2, 5-10, 48-53.

BRUCE, D. 1924. Prevention of disease (Inaugural address to the British Association, Toronto, 6th August 1924) *Nature* 114, suppl. 213-227.

BRUCE, M. 1956. Life in Ladysmith (Correspondence). *Journal of the Royal Army Medical Corps.* 102, 153-154.

CENTRAL REGION ARCHIVE, STIRLING. Sir David Bruce. PD 120/1 and PD 120/2.

DAVIES, M. 1955. A bibliography of the work of Sir David Bruce, 1887-1924. *Journal of the Royal Army Medical Corps* 101, 122-129.

DUGGAN, A.J. 1977. Bruce and the African Trypanosomes. *American Journal of Tropical Medicine and Hygiene* 26, 1080-1083.

McARTHUR, W. 1955. An account of some of Sir David Bruce's researches based on his own manuscripts. *Transactions Royal Society Tropical Medicine and Hygiene* 49, 404-412.

MITCHELL, J. 1989. David Bruce – the early naturalist years. People of the Forth (3). *Forth Naturalist and Historian* 11, 89-93.

SCIENTIFIC AMERICAN 17 Sept. 1910. Investigating the sleeping sickness of Uganda. 219, 225-6.

David and Mary Bruce and staff at the Mpumu Laboratory, Uganda investigating sleeping sickness.

Sir David and Lady Bruce.

Gravestone/memorial in Holy Rude
Kirkyard, Stirling

Close up of inscriptions.

THE ANCIENT BRIDGE OF STIRLING: A NEW SURVEY

R. Page

On the 11th of September 1297 the English army of Edward I was defeated by the Scots led by William Wallace at the Battle of Stirling Bridge. Contemporary English accounts tell of a narrow bridge crossed by part of the English army, which was then attacked by a superior force of Scots. Nearly 200 years later Blind Harry the Minstrel graphically described how the wooden bridge was sawn through, and how good John Wright removed a pin, causing the bridge to collapse and trap the English. We may suspect Blind Harry of poetic licence, since the English account, written within a few years of the event, says that the Earl of Surrey ordered the bridge to be broken down and burnt, presumably to cover his retreat to the south.[1]

This bridge may not have been the first across the Forth at Stirling. Boece in *Histories of the Scots* published in 1527 said that Agricola built a bridge there as part of the Roman campaign in Scotland, and another was built by Osbret, King of Northumbria, in 860 AD.[2] We have no way of knowing whether this was fact or fiction. It may be that Boece assumed that the bridge with seven arches depicted on the seal of the Burgh of Stirling[3] was Osbret's bridge. The earliest known use of the seal was in 1296; the seal clearly represents a wooden bridge, see Figure 1. The importance and prestige of the bridge at Stirling ensured that it was prominently featured on the map drawn at some time before 1259 by Matthew Paris.

Figure 1. Old Common Seal of the Burgh of Stirling.

The first authentic reference to a bridge at Stirling occurs in the reign of William the Lion (1165 - 1214). Stolen cattle had to be restored to their owners within six months at the Bridge of Stirling.[4] A little later a statute of Alexander II (1214 - 1249) regulated trial by combat at the bridge.[5]

After the battle in 1297 the bridge remained broken down for some years. In the writ issued by Edward I in 1305[6] it was said to be "broken down and destroyed", and he directed that it should be repaired. Timber was being taken to the bridge in 1336[7], presumably once again to effect repairs -after thirty years a wooden bridge would be likely to need attention. It appears to have deteriorated again by 1361, for then a ferry was in operation[8], and again a ferry was recorded in 1375 and 1376[9]. Although a bridge and a ferry are not necessarily mutually exclusive, it is unlikely that both would be in operation simultaneously at Stirling, where an acceptable ford, passable on foot at low tide, and suitable for traffic too large for a narrow wooden bridge, is available only two kilometres upstream at Kildean. A charter was issued in 1389 by Robert II confirming the earlier grant by David II of rights and duties concerning the ferry to St Lawrence's altar in the Parish Church of Stirling[10]. The ferry was still operating in 1391[11] when John of Cornton was paid for the passage of the King's horses.

A mention of 'the hospital of St James at the end of the roadway of the bridge of Stirling" in 1402[12] does not necessarily indicate that the bridge was then usable, neither does the mention in 1412 of the road called "Hilweynd leading to the Forth bridge at the western end of the same"[13] indicate that a new bridge was already completed. We know that in 1407 the bridge was ruinous, as that was stated in a letter from Pope Benedict XIII to the Diocese of St Andrews in which Stirling was situated. This letter came to light in the Vatican archives and was reported to a meeting in Stirling by the Rev. Thomas Miller in 1929[14]. In it the Pope grants an indulgence shortening time in purgatory by three years and three periods of forty days to all true penitents in return for the payment of a days wages for a worker repairing the bridge, and a relaxation of one hundred days for other contributions. This would explain how the money for the bridge was raised, for those times the terms would seem to be generous. The existence of only two other references to money being provided for the construction then becomes explicable. The first of these in 1408 was for £20[15], the other in 1415 for an unspecified amount[16], but taken together these could account for only a small fraction of the cost.

It is virtually certain that these payments refer to the present 'Old Bridge', replacing a previous timber bridge by a more permanent stone structure. Although Inglis was of the opinion[17] that "if we are to judge by its appearance and general probabilities, it might be more safely placed about 1500; but if one were to judge it by comparison with other structure, it might be put down as late as 1620", it is inconceivable that a bridge of this size and importance could be built after 1415 without leaving some trace in the documentary evidence.

Miller was of the opinion that the 'Old Bridge' was built of stone on the line of, and indeed using the foundations of, the previous timber bridge. Although he must have been aware that James Ronald in 1905 recognised the foundations of two piers of an older bridge[18] upstream from the 'Old Bridge' he apparently chose to ignore the report. The discovery aroused considerable interest at the time; there were contrbutions by Ronald and W B Cook to the Stirling Natural History and Archaeological Society[19] and correspondence in the local paper *The Sentinel* that was later reprinted in the *Stirling Antiquary*.[20]

Ronald's attention had been drawn by Michael Connelly, whose hobby was pearl fishing in the Forth, to obstructions in the river bed, which he recognised as two massive piers. Taking advantage of low water in June 1905 he took some approximate measurements, which he said were not to be taken as accurate. He wrote "The piers stand above the Old Bridge at a distance of from 65 to 75 yards, and nearly parallel to it. The centre of the north pier is about 25 yards from the north bank of the river; the distance between the north and south piers from centre to centre is from 20 to 25 yards, and from the centre of the south pier to the south bank a distance of from 25 to 30 yards". The north pier appeared to be constructed in a similar manner to the piers of the present Old Bridge, with a jacket of dry stones surrounding it. The top appeared to be level, and was covered with a few inches of gravel. The south pier was covered by a sand bank, but "On piercing it with a long iron, we came upon the solid pier".

Cook's sketch based on Ronald's measurements is reproduced as Figure 2.

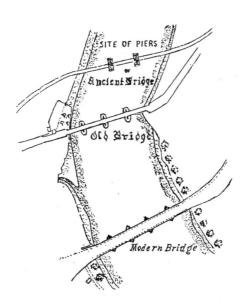

Figure 2. The ancient bridge of Stirling by Cook[19] based on Ronald's measurements.

These findings were confirmed during the drought of 1955 by R Swift of Bridge of Allan[21]. In 1988 the author and Campbell Chesterman of Cambuskenneth, working from a canoe, and viewing through a bucket with a perspex bottom, succeeded in locating the north pier and verifying Ronald's description of it.

Colin Martin from St Andrews University carried out an underwater reconnaissance of the pier on 8th June 1989, with the back-up support of Ken Stewart of the Scottish Sub Aqua Club. The presence of masonry, partially covered by sand and silt was apparent; some timber might have been part of the structure but it could have been snagged material.

Realising the value of an accurate survey, a survey team led by Peter Denholm of Bridge of Allan plotted the position and depth of the north pier in May 1990. The southern (more strictly, since the river here runs nearly north to south, the western) pier was deeply covered by a sand bank and could not be located on these occasions.

During the following summer we were unable to assemble the volunteer surveying team, but further attempts were made in 1992. Probing through the most prominent sandbank visible from the Old Bridge, using a thin metal probe 3.24m long at low tide revealed nothing; the sand was easily penetrated to the full depth of the probe. Masonry was found some distance away from the expected position, thinly covered by sand. Figure 3 shows the position of both piers. The broken line around the north (or eastern) pier No 1 has been drawn to surround the survey points and conforms to Ronald's measurements (metricated to 8.4 by 4.2m). These could be fairly easily verified, as it is possible at low water to stand on the relatively level top of the stonework. The southern (or western) pier No 2 could not be so accurately measured. A direct measurement between the limits found by probing indicated an approximate size of 11 by 4.5m. It seemed that the stonework had sloping sides so that size increased with depth. The top was more or less level. The mean measured depth of the top of pier No 1 was 0.36m above Ordnance Datum (mean of 8 measurements), that of pier No 2 was 0.31m above OD (mean of 12 measurements). The difference of only 5cms could very likely arise because pier No 1 depths were measured using a broad based survey staff, while those of pier No 2 were measured using a thin pointed metal probe.

The distance between the aproximate centres of the two piers is about 33m, considerably more than the 18 to 25m estimated by Ronald in 1905. On the other hand, his estimates of the distances to the banks agree well with ours (to the north bank the measurements agree at 23m, to the south bank Ronald found 23 to 27.4m, as against our 26m). If Ronald obtained his estimate of distance beween the piers by difference, measuring only distances from the banks and assuming that the piers were parallel to the Old Bridge, as he said they were, his figures would be understandable, as the width of the river at the Old Bridge is 68m. In fact the line of the piers is not parallel to the Old Bridge; its angle to the present river current is about 60°, whereas the line of the piers is about 30°.

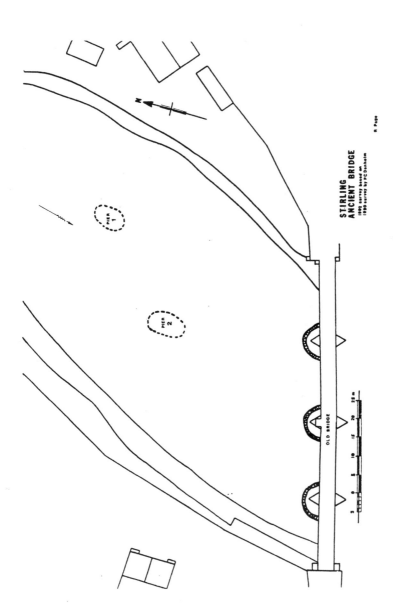

Figure 3. Surveyed Plan of Piers of Ancient Bridge, 1990 and 1992.

One might expect bridges to be built across a river more or less at right angles to the current. Inglis[16] discussed this problem in relation to the Old Bridge. He contrasted the Ordnance Survey map of 1866 with Adair's Map of c1683.

"It is to be observed that ... the bridge is not at right angles to the stream, and yet the course of the river after the bridge is at right angles to the bridge. In other words, it is perfectly evident that when originally constructed the cut-waters faced the stream, but the river has shifted its course and no longer passes straight through the arches, but obliquely ... we see (from the maps) that some change has taken place in 200 years, for the bends of the river, though substantially in the same line, do not show quite the same shapes at the curves, which have evidently been gradually eaten away by erosion of floods and spates.'

Following this reasoning, if the river direction had changed from 90° to 60° in the period from say 1450 to 1866, and as the earlier change in direction appears to be similar, provided that the rate of change of river direction remained constant over the whole period, it might indicate that the bridge piers were placed originally across the river at right angles to the stream in about 1000 AD. Of course this assumes that the piers are indeed bridge piers both belonging to the same bridge and built to cross the river directly at right angles. Could there, for example, have been constraints because of the nature of the river bed, so that sites with firm foundations had to be chosen? It may be relevant to consider the relationship of the bridges to the approach roads from the town. Recent changes have obscured the earlier relationships, but the map of 1820 by John Wood[22] shows only the lower 100m of Lower Bridge Street pointing to the Old Bridge, whereas the preceeding 200m point directly towards the line of the piers of the ancient bridge.

In 1907 excavations were made to search for abutments or an approach roadway to the ancient bridge.

"The first trench started 100 yards above the present Old Bridge, and was continued towards the bridge for a distance of forty yards. This covered the ground facing the old piers in the river, where the road was believed by ex-Baillie Ronald to have passed. From this position a number of trenches and openings were made stretching from 60 yards above the bridge to 30 yards above the bridge. They were dug a little above the high water line and to a depth of 6½ feet. The excavation only displayed a bank of fine sand about 6½ feet deep, and underneath that came a bed of dark clay." No signs of abutments or an approach road were found.[23]

The span of 33m between the piers is very large, much greater than in any of the nineteen stone bridges considered by Inglis. The earliest bridge he describes, London Bridge, had eleven arches, varying (except for one small arch) between 7.3 and 10m. One of the arches of the bridge at Perth, constructed in 1766, is 27m. The largest of the four (unequal) arches of Stirling Old Bridge is 17m. Inglis considered that in general the size of span of stone arches tended to increase as time went on and experience in bridge construction increased. The large span between the piers would seem to confirm that the ancient bridge in Stirling was a wooden bridge.

Ruddock[24] has discussed the various methods of constructing the foundations for bridges. Where piers could be founded on rock, above or a little below water level, the ideal situation prevailed. Failing this, a sound foundation might be obtained by building a coffer dam of wooden piles within which the pier could be built. Before pumps were available, water could be removed by baling. Neither of these methods would be suitable in a tidal river. Ruddock describes building on 'starlings' which were artificial islands created by dumping rocks within a surround of wooden piles, or by the use of 'branders', these being a framework of wood like a raft, which was sunk in the appropriate position by piling masonry on the timber frame until a suitable pier was formed. The starling method was used at Berwick (1611-25) while the Bridge of Dee (1527) at Aberdeen was built with branders.

The Rev Thomas Miller states in his paper[14] on the Old Bridge of Stirling that during the repairs undertaken in 1912 it was found that

"the piers of stone rested, as excavation showed, on a platform of oak beams laid horizontally, and also that the beams and stones where they met were accurately flushed, ... Under the oak beams, massive in strength and in excellent state of preservation, sand and clay were found to be compressed to such a degree as to be impenetrable, lying as the sand and clay did between the superincumbent weight of the bridge, and a rock foundation lower down."

This seems to be a good description of a brander. It is likely that the earlier bridge piers were constructed by a similar method, although the use of starlings would also be a possibility.

In either case it is likely that under, within, or beside the piers of the ancient bridge some of the original timber remains in anaerobic conditions that have prevented decay. There must then be exciting possibilities that modern methods of underwater archaeology might recover a sample of this timber, that by carbon dating, or with a sufficiently large sample, much more accurately by dendrochronology, would be able to settle unequivocally the question of the date of construction of the Ancient Bridge of Stirling.

ACKNOWLEDGEMENTS

The location of the north pier was possible in 1988 by the enthusiastic help of Campbell Chesterman who provided the canoe and the perspex bottomed bucket. Colin Martin came from St Andrews Unversity to inspect the pier underwater and was supported by Mr K Stewart of Stirling Royal Infirmary and the Scottish Sub-Aqua Club. The initial survey in 1990 was carried out by Peter Denholm, a retired architect from Bridge of Allan. The boat and supporting canoes were provided by Drew Milroy and family, boatmanship by

Campbell Chesterman, and surveying assistance was supplied by David Gilvear and David Harrison from Stirling University. Ken Mackay of Stirling Field and Archaeological Society made photographic and video recordings of the days work. Especial thanks are due to Thomas Delaney for allowing the work to proceed from his garden at Bridgehaugh Cottage, and for much other help.

In 1992 the survey was completed by the same participants except for Peter Denholm and David Harrison; other helpers in that year were John Reid of Falkirk Local History Society, Alan Snedden of Cambuskenneth and Tim Acock from Stirling University.

NOTES AND REFERENCES

1. For a detailed discussion see COOK, W.B. 1905. The battle of Stirling Bridge - the Kildean Myth. *Trans. Stirling Natural History and Achaeological Society 1904 - 5*, 27, 31-52.

2. According to the Anglo-Saxon Chronicle, Osberht was deposed in AD 866 or 867.

3. Frontispiece in Charters and Other Documents Relating to the Royal Burgh of Stirling 1124 - 1705, Glasgow 1884.

4. Acts of the Parliament of Scotland, I, 372. Edinburgh 1822.

5. Acts of the Parliament of Scotland, I, 400. Edinburgh 1822.

6. Calendar of Documents relating to Scotland II, 1272-1306, p461, No 1705. Edinburgh 1884.

7. Calendar of Documents relating to Scotland IIi, 1307-1357, p364. Edinburgh 1887.

8. The Exchequer Rolls of Scotland II, 1359-1379, p 61. Edinburgh 1878.

9. The Exchequer Rolls of Scotland II, 1359-1379, 490 & 538. Edinburgh 1878.

10. The Register of the Great Seal of Scotland 1306-1424, p281, No 755. Edinburgh 1912.

11. The Exchequer Rolls of Scotland 1379-1406, III, p 258. Edinburgh 1880.

12. Charters and Other Documents Relating to the Royal Burgh of Stirling 1124-1705. Glasgow 1884.

13. Cartulary of Cambuskenneth, p 299. Grampian Club 1872.

14. *Trans. Stirling Natural History and Achaeological Society 1928-29*, 51, 83-94.

15. The Exchequer Rolls of Scotland IV, 1406-1436, p68. Edinburgh 1880.

16. The Exchequer Rolls of Scotland IV, 1406-1436, p236. Edinburgh 1880.

17. INGLIS, H.R.G. 1913. The Roads and Bridges in the early History of Scotland. *Proceedings of the Society of Antiquaries of Scotland 47*, 303-333.

18. Scotsman, June 1905, quoted in R. MENZIES FERGUSSON, Logie; a Parish History, p 263. Paisley 1905.

19. *Transactions of the Stirling Natural History and Achaeological Society 28, 1905-6*. 33-35.

20. *Stirling Antiquary, IV, 1908*, 161-170.

21. RCAHMS, 1963, Inventory of Stirlingshire, II, p410, No 455.

22. WOOD, J. 1820. Plan of the Town of Stirling. Central Region Archives MP/SB/2.

23. *Transactions of the Stirling Natural History and Archaeological Society, 1907-8, 30*. p3.

24. RUDDOCK, T. 1984. Bridges and Roads in Scotland: 1400-1750. In Loads and Roads in Scotland and Beyond. A. FENTON and G. STELL editors. Edinburgh.

LAUNCHING FORTH: THE RIVER – ALLOA TO STIRLING

David Angus

Some years ago Lindsay Corbett and I[1] determined[2] to sail the River Forth from Alloa to Stirling and back. Having no boat and there being no regular sailings on the river, we approached the Forth River Purification Board (FRPB) who generously invited us to join their launch which surveys the river from Port Edgar to Stirling once a month. So on the appointed summer 1981 day we joined this small craft (Figure 1) at South Alloa slipway, on the opposite bank from Alloa itself. At that time Tom Leatherland and Mike Elliott[3] were the FRPB scientist crew.

The weather was, I remember, execrable[4] and we were wrapped in oilskins; but visibility was not bad. The going up-river was slow with many stoppages. Samples of the water had to be hoisted aboard at key points, tested, labelled and stored for later more detailed analysis/recording. We gave a hand wherever we could (Figure 2). I cannot now remember details of soundings or pollution sampling that day being more concerned with general visual impressions. To the north lay the quilted and dappled range of the Ochils, only a few miles away. Ahead, on the skyline, the magnificent crowned tower of the Wallace Monument on the Abbey Craig waited to greet us, a giant sentinel. The carse-lands near the river were sometimes screened by bright fences of reeds. We were far from alone on the river. Above Alloa we passed boat after boat moored in midstream, each with a salmon fisherman or two aboard. The Forth has unseen riches beneath its twinkling surface – as well, it seems, as varying amounts of pollution. But the latter was being closely monitored.

Figure 1. The FRPB launch at S. Alloa.

The Forth: Stirling to Kincardine from Bartholemews 1:100,000 c⁵/₈″/mile.

We were wending (and winding) our way up these famous Links of the Forth, which transforms five miles (as the crow flies) into a sinuous series of ox-bows, a river-voyage of near 14 miles. The effect of this continual turning and twisting is peculiar, for landmarks like the Abbey Craig, the green wall of the Ochils, and Stirling Castle Rock seem to waltz round one perpetually in magical fashion. We passed acres of deep-litter sheds, and bonded warehouses, less beautiful and less interesting. But in general it was a gentle enjoyable sail well worth making. Highlights were novel views of the hills, the surviving giant tower of Cambuskenneth Abbey, of the Wallace Monument, and of course the Castle on its rock. We could see why pleasure boats had carried passengers from Leith or Granton up to Stirling Shore as late as the 1930's, with stop-offs at places like Bo'ness, Alloa and Cambuskenneth. We passed the deserted Stirling Shore at Riverside; it is now landscaped into a miniature public park, under Forth Crescent (Figure 3).

We made the last monitoring stop between Robert Stevenson's road-bridge (1831) and the rail-bridge immediately downriver from it, and there enjoyed a brief break. Ignored by the racing traffic overhead we nibbled sandwiches and drank from flasks.

Returning now downstream to South Alloa with no tasks to perform speed was the order of the day. Suddenly our outboard launch transformed itself into a speedboat. It thundered downriver, and we experienced a swift and noisy reversal of what had taken a couple of hours going the other way. It was an exhilarating experience; the Ochils and landmarks now quickstepping about us instead of doing their slow waltz.

Figure 2. D. Angus assists in the water sampling.

The days of ships and paddle-steamers (Figure 4) on the upper Forth (McCutcheon pp84-93) are long past, and unlikely to come again. Since our little voyage the road bridge across the river at Kincardine has been fixed; it no longer swings open for ships to pass. The Admiralty depot at Bandeath (to which naval vessels once sailed is now an industrial estate. Moving banks of silt within the tidal windings would make progress difficult for any deep-draught vessel. Shallow-draught boats, like ours or an observation style launch, have little trouble. At Upper Taylorton, on the carse-land east of Stirling, the recent ill thought low-set bridge of the by-pass road also makes larger ship traffic impossible without reconstruction.

Figure 3. One of the FN&H hired fishing boats at Stirling Shore, Sept. 1981.

It has to be said that the river itself is not invariably beautiful. Being tidal, it is often turbid, can be hit by sudden rain squalls[4] and at low tide it has gleaming flanks of mud. I am told that members of Stirling Rowing Club really make a point of not falling into the river! Though flowing through – or rather past – Stirling, the river could hardly be described as a focus of interest or of much activity. The Rowing Club uses it; the odd raft-race takes place; and there are a few walks and thoroughfares – Lovers' Walk, Dean Crescent, Queenshaugh Drive and Riverside Drive. Sport skirts the Forth a little, Bridgehaugh Park contains the ground of Stirling County Rugby Club, and there is a delightful bowling green at Queenshaugh, nipped between two reaches of the river.

But; no Stirling hotel looking down on the river; no real promenade/walks; no parkland bordering it. True, the Stirling Initiative plans a hotel in the

Riverside area, but not to face the Forth, and the Initiative-planned(!) park across the river looks like a flat featureless expanse of green – and liable to flooding. At Cambus and Alloa the story is much the same. At Alloa that used to be a busy harbour and series of shipbuilding yards, it becomes more and more difficult to find one's way to the riverside past industrial developments. Once distinguished residential streets nearby have come severely down in the world or have disappeared completely. Because of its extravagant windings and banks of mud, there are few, if any, country walks by the Forth between the two towns[5]. All of which suggests a fugitive feature of the Scottish landscape, an almost forgotten river, with little if any traffic on it above Grangemouth and practically no recreational and scenic amenities.

And yet the Forth, which at one time practically cut off Scotia or Caledonia proper from the rest of the country, and which later 'bridled the wild Hielandman', cutting the hungry Highlands off from the rich Lowlands, was undoubtedly a feature of considerable historical and geographical importance. Key strategic battles, including those of the Wars of Scottish Independence, such as Stirling Bridge and Bannockburn, were fought beside it; survivors of these conflicts were drowned in its waters or escaped across them.

In medieval times the ships of a Scottish Navy were built on its banks and harboured in it, and later it provided a major thoroughfare for traffic and trade with Europe, particularly in coal. The Queensferries, Bo'ness, Culross, Carronshore, Alloa, Airth and Stirling were (by the standards of their days) major Scottish ports. Famous visitors such as Mendelssohn were introduced to Scotland up its waters. Its present comparative insignificance and condition of neglect mark a sad and unnecessary decline in its status.

In William Harvey's collection *The Harp of Stirlingshire* we find a whole range of poems and songs attached to the Forth, at one time of great popularity. But these too are forgotten, and there is no modern equivalent of 'The Song of the Clyde.' That title, however, does remind me that the Forth boasts its own biography, a brilliant history entitled *The Story of the Forth* by the geologist and mining engineer H. M. Cadell. I recommend it to all readers. Cadell takes us back to a time when the post-Ice Age sea stretched up to Aberfoyle, and tells the dazzling story of Lord Kames' clearance of peat from Flanders Moss in the late 18th century in the interests of agriculture.

Very well, the impatient reader may say, there is no turning the clock back. Is the Forth any more than a superannuated one-time waterway winding across half of Scotland? Was Winston Churchill wrong in planning a direct ship-canal cutting through all those romantic Links to make a utilitarian short-cut for shipping between Atlantic Ocean and North Sea? But clocks can be moved forward more readily than back on the brink of the 21st century. It is worth noting ambitious plans for Stirling and Alloa which could readily include revitalising projects for the forgotten Forth.

The Stirling Initiative plans, already mentioned, make much of the Riverside area, and foresee the visitor's experience of Stirling as often commencing there. Typically, however, the river itself is ignored – the proposed hotel looks elsewhere, a busy new thoroughfare is planned to come between the river and new developments near it, and no plans exist for riverside parkland, gardens and walks. But these 'Initiative' ideas have not been implemented, have been much criticised, and are susceptible to improvement. A marina at old Stirling Shore is not an impossible dream, instead of the blank sheet of water we see at present. Leisure activities on and about the river cry out for development. There is an urgent requirement for vision and imagination.

Nearer Alloa an even greater marina would be possible in the broad reaches off Bandeath. There is already serious talk of bringing Alloa harbour back to life, with barge type shipping and pleasure craft again on the river; but a 'privatised' Port Authority is a stumbling block. Alloa itself, so long regarded as severely industrial with its breweries and woollen mills, is taking a belated tumble to itself tourist-wise. But leisure facilities for the natives can be so readily eroded as when leisure grounds (e.g. Paton and Baldwin's) disappear beneath new housing; a church, housing and other developments take parts of West End and Greenfield parks; and maybe Inglewood's grounds. However, Alloa Tower, for long a gaunt and neglected monument to the Erskine family (the Earls of Mar and Kellie) and the young Royal Stuarts they brought up there, is to become a beautifully-restored visitors' centre, surrounded by gracious landscaping[5], and every attempt will be made to tell its story, and that of its distinguished habitués. It is not forgotten that Mary, Queen of Scots sailed up the Forth from Leith to Alloa Tower in 1567 to seek advice and support from the Earl of Mar. The present-day Earl is himself a keen canoeist on the Forth, and delights in the memory of Mary's voyage to see his ancestor.

No doubt days of historical pageants at Alloa and on the Forth could still come. Stirling with its Royal Stirling Players and plays, is already very effectively showing the way. But other even more modest and practical proposals should be considered first. On rivers such as the Thames and the Seine shallow-draught vessels with shelter and observation windows for passengers are a familiar sight. One has appeared up here indeed on the Clyde in Glasgow. Many of us have memories of boarding such craft in the shadow of the Houses of Parliament and being pleasantly and instructively borne down to Greenwich and back. Kindred but smaller craft could readily negotiate the Forth, and the current obstacles in the way of some conventional shipping could be overcome.

True, passengers would not be looking at city landmarks, but there would be plenty to see, and to hear about. If voyages went from Kincardine-on-Forth to Stirling there would be a host of attractions – the wild fowl; Airth Castle (part of which dates back to William Wallace); Tulliallan Castle; Kennetpans (why the name?); Dunmore (that delightful planned village); Kilbagie, with its whisky of Burns' time; Clackmannan and its Tower (tales of the Bruces, and of Robert Burns); Alloa, its Tower and industries; Alloa Inch with its farm; the dramatic remains of Alloa Rail Bridge, and stories of the steamers 'shooting' the bridge; Tullibody Inch; the outflows of the River Devon and the Bannock Burn; the exciting turns and twists through Blackgrange, Manor, and much of our agricultural and industrial history; the delectable village of Cambuskenneth with that impressive Abbey Tower and a royal burial; Stirling and its historic 'Shore'; and beyond, that sentinel Wallace Monument; the great Castle itself; and the picturesque Old Stirling Bridge.

Above and beyond all these, the waltzing Ochils, with King's Seat, The Law, Ben Cleuch, Ben Ever, Craigleith, Myreton and Dumyat. The commentary could feature not only historical insights but some of the above-mentioned poetry and song, as well as pioneer travellers' descriptions – hear Daniel Defoe on the Ochils, and Alloa's Lime Tree Walk! Let us not forget the rich culture of the Ochils – poetry, history and folklore.

It all simply awaits to be done, with voyages undertaken around high tides (to obscure those mud-banks, and bring the ample wildlife on the banks closer. Is the Forth to be a forgotten, neglected 'river of no return,' or a thoroughfare into the heart of our scenery and history? Will it pale into a ghost of its former self, or revive into something like the great and vital artery it once was? As always, it is up to us.

NOTES – BY THE EDITOR

1. David Angus, a member of the FN&H Editorial Board, writer, historian, poet, expert on Robert Louis Stevenson, man of many parts, died sadly in January 1994. Some months earlier he wrote this paper to emphasise the unfulfilled potentials of the River Forth; published now with the consent of Mrs Angus.

2. We also wanted this as a reconnoitre for an organised cruise by the FN&H as a Man In The Landscale event. This materialised on Sunday 13th September 1981 when two fishing boats carried some 30 participants from and to Kincardine and Stirling Shore, Riverside (Figure 3).

3. Mike Elliott was later in 1989 one of two commentators on the FN&H cruise aboard the Maid of the Forth from S. Queensferry to Kincardine as a complement to the Man and the Landscape Symposium on the Forth Estuary.

4. But nothing like as wild as some years later when two launches with a Regional Council party were caught in a squall of rain, wind and mist, and had to run for shelter to Bandeath pier.

5. Some years ago Regional and District Councils commissioned a study for Alloa/Stirling riverside walks, and some do appear on local and regional plans as future intent.

Some Readings of the Forth

BRODIE, I. Steamers of the Forth. David and Charles. 1976

CORBETT, L. Editor. Central Scotland: land, wildlife, people. Forth Naturalist and Historian. 1994.

FIRTH OF FORTH WILDLIFE. NCC and Central Region. Teachers Notes.

GALLOWAY. Tourist Guide to the River Forth. 1890's.

HALIBURTON, Hugh. Ochil Idylls and Other Poems. 1891.

HARVEY, William. The Harp of Stirlingshire. Parlane. Paisley, 1897. 530pp.
LOTHIAN, J. Banks of the Forth: Descriptive and Historical Sketches. 1862.
McINTOSH, I. B. Three and the Forth: dinghies sail Stirling to Alloa. *Scots Magazine,* August 1974 (Figure 5).
MAIR, C., Stirling: the Royal Burgh. John Donald. 1990.
MORRIS, D. B. Nature and man in the Forth Valley. *Transactions of the Scottish Natural History Society.* 1901.
POLLOCK, D. Dictionary of the Forth. Aberfoyle to Isle of May. 1892.
Map. Central Scotland 1:100,000. Bartholemew for Central Region. 1982.

Figure 4. The Edinburgh Castle on the Forth.

Figure 5. Dinghies sail the Forth. (McIntosh).

ARCHAEOLOGY NOTES

Sites at Kilbyrde

Lorna Main, Central Region

In 1990 Stirling Field and Archaeological Society members, Ron and Cathie Page, while field walking as part of their research into Roman roads, came upon a recently felled area of woodland known as Gallow Hill, not far from Kilbryde Castle by Dunblane. They were drawn to two stands of mature broad-leaved trees left undisturbed by the felling on two high points of the field. Further investigation confirmed the presence of the remains of two very different types of structure, each enclosed by trees and occupying prominent and commanding positions. In an attempt to identify the nature and date of these remains I was notified of the discovery, and what follows is a summary of my assessment supplemented by a survey by the Centre for Field Archaeology at the University of Edinburgh funded by Historic Scotland.

DESCRIPTION

Site 1 NS 7459 0374

This survives as an oval enclosure represented by a low scatter of grass covered stones standing only to a maximum height of 0.5m. The enclosure measures about 11m by 9m within a bank generally 3m wide with possibility an entrance in the north west side. The stone walled enclosure is surrounded by a tree lined enclosure set, at least in part, on a low earthen bank, probably a late plantation bank. The archaeological remains are very fragmentary and their survival has been entirely due to the presence of the surrounding broad-leaved trees. An examination of the remains and their location in relation to both the immediate topography and their wider landscape setting strongly suggest a homestead of Iron Age date. My initial reaction was that the remains represented a broch but on reflection the site has been so severely damaged in the past that this interpretion probably goes further than the actual remains allow. I have had to settle for the more general description of Iron Age homestead.

Site 2 NS 7469 0370

In contrast to site 1 the remains here comprise a squared double ditched earthwork enclosure about 55m SE of site 1. Measuring about 30m by 28m overall, the inner bank, up to 0.4m high and 2m wide, encloses an area 13m by 14m. Between the inner and outer banks is a shallow ditch just over 1m wide. The second low bank is up to 0.3m high while its shallow external ditch varies from 1 to 2m wide. The site had suffered some damage from machine tracks especially on the north west. The site's date and function so far remain uncertain. It is perhaps medieval if not Roman.

CONCLUSION

The surrounding area has now been replanted; but thanks to the keen eye and prompt action of two local people two very interesting and important archaeological sites have not only been properly recorded by Historic Scotland but are now preserved within the new plantation. An access route to the sites has also been left unplanted by the landowner.

REFERENCES

McKEAGUE, P., and SANGSTER, A., 1990. Short Notice Forestry Survey at Gallow Hill, Argaty Parish, Stirling District, Central Region. Centre for Field Archaeology, Dept. of Archaeology, Edinburgh University.

PAGE, R., PAGE C., and MAIN, L. 1990. In: *Discovery and Excavation in Scotland*. p9.

Other Recent Archaeological Activities

Some activity has been occasioned by preliminary site investigations concerned with projected developments in Stirling Old Town. Some digs in Broad Street. have revealed old cobbled ways, 16th century pottery and middens; being funded by Forth Valley Enterprise. Some digging between the Tolbooth and the Boys Club, and in St. John Street in front of the Boys Club, has uncovered cobbled roadway, pottery and midden materials, this being done by the Scottish Urban Archaeological Trust from Perth.

BOOK REVIEWS AND NOTES (Historical)

THE RING OF WORDS: Literary landmarks of Stirling and Clackmannan. Louis Stott. Creag Darach Publications. 32pp. £2.95. ISBN 1-874585-02-4. (p&p £10).

This is the first of an intended series about the literary topography of Scotland with in preparation – 2 Loch Lomond, 3 Argyll, 4 Perth and 5 Trossachs. The author has already published two books focussed on Robert Louis Stevenson – *Stevenson and the Highlands and Islands* and *Stevenson and France*. The area under consideration includes the Ochils and the Devon basin, upper Loch Tay and Loch Earn, Balquhuidder, Dunblane, Stirling town and the basin of the middle Forth.

The 20 page alphabetical gazetteer of literary sites is a thorough fascinating read covering some three dozen places in varying lengths from a few lines to some four pages for Dollar and for Stirling itself. This is preceded by a key page listing of literary sites and succeeded by a six page index to another in the text with brief biographic and other information about them.

This is surely a 'must' for the bookshelf of anyone interested in the history, culture, heritage of the 'heart of Scotland,' and a valuable counter to the tendency for people, in this case, writers, to be neglected, unrecognised, in their native places.

L. C.

DEVON VALLEY RAILWAY – A short note and photo in *Blastpipe* Summer 1994 of SRPS, about the display and Wilson collection in Dollar Museum. April to Christmas Saturdays 11-1, 2-4.30, Sundays 2-4.30.

RAILWAYS OF THE CARRON COMPANY – Brian Watters. 5pp illustrated. ibid 19-23.

ALLOA POTTERY – a history c1783-1907. J. A. S. Spreull and R. Rankine. Clackmannan District Libraries. 1994. 62pp. £6.50 (p&p £1).

Charles Lamb begins his essay 'On Old China' with "I have an almost feminine partiality for old china." I agree with his taste, although I would not think it particularly masculine or feminine. In common with many others, I am drawn towards an elegant ornament or a charming piece of china; equally, I am interested in its origins. The success of television's 'Antiques Road Show' has surely been founded on this.

The book has provided me with some pleasurable reading. Combining the enthusiasm of the aficionado with the self-discipline of the academic is no easy task, but this has, in the main, been accomplished. It is unfortunate, however, that a long list of corrigenda has had to be appended. This offers few problems for the general reader, but might prove irritating to the expert. The book is A4 size, the print exceptionally clear and the numerous illustrations include four pages of full coloured plates.

On the history and origins of Alloa Pottery, the authors demonstrate their scholarship; other chapters include 'Registered Designs' by Graeme Cruikshank where an overview of the Scottish pottery industry is taken; and 'Marks and Attributions' reveals the difficulty in claiming any articles as genuine 'Alloa.' Appendices feature an extract from *Ceramic Art in Britain* by Llewellyn Jewett 1883, and extracts from the *Alloa Advertiser* of 1889 describing a strike, and later a visit to the Kirkgate pottery. Who could refrain from smiling at the chapter on Motto Ware, so reminiscent of "what Granny used to say," with old saws such as "guid gear's in sma' buik," "keep yer braith tae cool yer parritch" or "wilful waste maks woeful want." This is a charming feature in an erudite book.

And now to the history. The Alloa Pottery grew from humble beginnings under the original owners, Shaw by name, until, in the 1820's when William Gardner and his son took over, soon becoming renowned for high quality Rockingham ware, particularly teapots. Majolica ware, greatly admired by the public, was introduced; also white and coloured earthenware. In 1856, financial problems forced the sale of the business to Joseph Bailey, an Edinburgh stoneware merchant, who continued the work as before, and put the business on a more secure footing. The most labour-saving and state-of-the-art machines were bought to keep prices low, and the pottery was expanded, while new articles, such as covered cheese dishes were developed. By about 1862, Joseph's sons, William and John, were in charge; world-wide connections were set up by William's visits to the Continent, and to Australia and New Zealand. Exports to India, China, Japan, USA and Canada were also undertaken. Two steam engines drove the machines; there was even an elevator through all the seven storeys of the building; Bailey's even had its own siding and shed at the harbour rail track.

By the turn of the century, business began to decline, and the death of John A. Bailey anticipated by only two years, the end of the Alloa Pottery in Kirkgate. Alloa residents were familiar with the tall warehouse building until its demolition in the 1970's, but by that time it was in use by a local brewery; few perhaps knew of its origins as a successful business, known world-wide. Its products, however, have been treasured in many a home, by many a hearth.

Isabel G. Stewart

TULLIALLAN SCHOOL BOARD – the troubled years (1872-6). James Sharp. c130pp. priv print.

The 1872 Education Act greatly changed the management of parish and burgh schools throughout Scotland. Some thousand school boards, elected by the local ratepayers of parishes and burghs, and nationally under the authority of an executive Scotch Education Department, took over the running of schools from the heritors and the burgh councils.

The transition was not always a smooth one, and the early years of a board that seemed to be bedevilled by troubles and bigotry are shown in detail by this studiously selected collection of minutes and of extracts from the Alloa and Stirling papers of the time. This is a valuable local resource for the study of this eventful time in Scottish education. Copies of the book can be consulted in the public libraries of Alloa, Dunfermline and Kincardine-on-Forth, and in the Central Regional Archives, Stirling.

ORDNANCE SURVEY MAPS – a concise guide for historians. Richard Oliver, Charles Close Society for the study of Ordnance Survey maps. 1993. 192pp. ISBN 1-870598-13-X. £12.95

Conceived as a basic OS 'source book' it succeeds the 1964 *Historian's Guide* by J. B. Harley and C. W. Phillips, and Harley's *OS Maps: a Descriptive Manual*, 1975. It has three objectives –

a) to guide users to the usefulness (or otherwise (e.g. 1:25000)) of each OS map scale as an information source for landscape study

b) to describe published 1:10560 (six inch) and larger scales for counties and larger towns

c) to give guidance on how landscape elements are depicted, though to do so comprehensively would require further research and a much larger work. While extremely helpful chapter 3 describing detail features alphabetically, and indexed, how they are represented is not illustrated here, though might be found randomly in some country entries in chapter 5.

This is a great working 'source,' but the occasional usei may find it frustrating at times.

L.C.

BLACKFRIARS MONASTERY – A significant recent local archaeological discovery is that of the remains behind Stirling's Murray Place of this lost thirteenth century church of the Dominicans. The *Stirling Observer* of 14th September 1994 reports briefly on the research and excavation leading to finding this pre-Reformation institution by local husband and wife, E. R. and C. Page.

THREE NIGHTS IN PERTHSHIRE: a reprint of the original description of a Scotch Hairst held at Ledard, by Thomas Atkinson (1801-33). Editors Louis Stott and Fergus Wood. Creag Darach Publications, Aberfoyle. 1994. 48pp. ISBN 1-874585 06 7. £3.95.

Hairst Kirn, a harvest celebration occasion, is the focus providing a lively description of the Aberfoyle Loch and Trossachs area and people of the time exampled by the extended family of the early 19C yeoman farmer who worked Ledard. The young Glasgow bookseller author published it modestly in 1821 and again in 1833, reprinted in 1897 and again in 1984 by Fergus Wood, present owner of Ledard (after being offered to FN&H in 1981!). It is presented in the form of a journal letter to an Oxford friend, and the writer's style is indicated by his (p22) enthusing on the dawn "I was 'drunk with rapture' – thrilled by the very spirit of gladness! Never shall I forget that balmy hour...."

L.C.

GARTMORE VILLAGE MAP. Coloured pictorial wall map with 12 pages of text and verso, 640 x 600mm. Folded and flat versions. Published by the voluntary Gartmore Village Map Group, October 1994. £3.00.

An attractively produced heritage resource for this historic village (associated with R. B. Cunninghame-Graham), including natural history and geography. Inspired by the 1987 Parish Maps Project of the English charity 'Common Ground', it is the first produced for a village in Scotland. If it develops successfully it could be a valuable complement to the Godfrey Old Ordnance Survey series, a source of history notes and 1890s large scale maps of some hundreds of places in the UK; 25 of those in central Scotland have been commissioned by FN&H.

STRATHYRE, BALQUHIDDER & LOCHEARNHEAD IN OLD PHOTOGRAPHS. Ewen W. Cameron. String District Libraries. 64pp. 1994. ISBN 1 870542 28 2. £2.95.

Ninety photographs from the mid 1880's to the 1980's are informatively annotated, illustrating a fair variety of places, activities and people. Lochearnhead has 32 pages, Balquhidder 15, Strathyre 8.